Ruth DeBusk, PhD, RD ⋮ Yael Joffe, RD (SA)

Edited by Luba Vikhanski

It's Not Just Your Genes!

Your Diet • Your Lifestyle • Your Genes

BKDR PUBLISHING

To re-order: go to **www.ItsNotJustYourGenes.com** or call: **(619) 223-7775**

For information or order inquiries, contact:
BKDR, Inc.
731 Golden Park Drive
San Diego, CA 92106
(619) 223-7775

Published by BKDR, Inc.

Printed in the United States of America

ISBN 0-9776363-0-5

Book Design by Jesse Beleck
Illustrations by Mark Bauer

Acknowledgments

We gratefully thank the following for sharing their talents, vision and support throughout the development of this book:

RAY RODRIQUEZ, PhD, Director of the University of California, Davis, Center of Excellence of Nutritional Genomics, for his belief in the future of nutritional genomics and the importance of educating consumers in this emerging area

JUDITH GILBRIDE, PhD, RD, FADA, incoming President of the American Dietetic Association and long-time champion of the importance of nutritional genomics to dietetics practice

DAVID CASTLE, PhD and **PAULA ROBSON-ANSLEY, PhD,** for the unique content they contributed to this book

JANE REINHARDT-MARTIN, RD, for sharing her expertise with flax and recipes from her cookbook, *The Amazing Flax Cookbook*

LISA POWELL, MS, RD, Director of Nutrition, Canyon Ranch®, Tucson for contributing the healthy recipes that make nutritional genomics look scrumptious

Yael's colleagues **JIM BRUCE, ROSALYNN GILL-GARRISON, PhD, KEITH GRIMALDI, PhD** and **BROOKS HYBERTSON, PhD** for their thought-provoking discussions about the science behind the practical applications of nutritional genomics

JESSE BELECK for her superb graphic design and excellent organizational skills

SANDY CASH for her insight, precision and sense of humor as an editorial assistant

JAN STRODE for her abounding energy, tireless effort and support of the book

Table of Contents

Figures and Text Boxes

Figures

Text Boxes

Foreword

....

I*t's Not Just Your Genes!* reflects an important paradigm shift in the way people understand nutrition and its implications for short- and long-term health. For millennia people have seen food mainly as a source of energy. More recently, society began to demand that its food be both wholesome and safe. Today we expect even more from our diets, and see food as a complex mixture of components that can promote health and reduce the risk for many chronic and age-related diseases – from hypertension to diabetes to some forms of cancer.

The new view of food is explored by nutritional genomics – a discipline that studies the interaction between genes, diet and lifestyle factors. As one of the newest areas of inquiry to emerge from the Human Genome Project, nutritional genomics believes that: (1) poor diet can be a risk factor for disease; (2) common dietary components can alter gene expression and gene structure; (3) the degree to which diet influences the balance between health and disease depends on an individual's genetic make-up; (4) some diet-regulated genes (and their common variants) play a role in the onset, incidence, progression and severity of certain diseases and (5) dietary recommendations based on a knowledge of nutritional requirement, nutritional status and genetic make-up can prevent, mitigate and potentially cure disease.

Indeed, the sequencing of the human genome has added a new dimension to the equation, linking the foods we eat to the good health we all hope to enjoy. This new genomic perspective on nutrition and health can be seen in recent marketing campaigns for drugs that address the "two sources of cholesterol – food and family history." Consumers are beginning to realize that, when we come to the table, we bring not only our appetite, but also our genotype; that is, the sum total of genes inherited from each parent. As we begin to understand the genetic diversity that makes each of us unique, we can also begin to appreciate why we respond to our nutritional environment differently and how these differences can, over time, lead to health or disease.

As the Human Genome Project tells us, we are all 99.9 percent identical at the DNA level. This implies that the remaining 0.1 percent of the human genome (or about 3 million single bits of genetic code) is responsible for all the apparent and hidden differences, from eye and hair color to our susceptibility to disease. As the authors will discuss, common variation in the form of genes encoding enzymes and receptor proteins can affect reaction rates in metabolic pathways that, in turn, can create individual differences in the way we absorb, metabolize, store and use nutrients and other bioactive food components.

Although there is good evidence that certain genotypes are more severely affected by specific dietary factors than others, we should remember that no genotype is completely immune to the deleterious effects of poor diet. Furthermore, it is unlikely that any single gene or risk factor will have the predictive power needed to confirm a predisposition for a particular chronic condition or cancer. This is because diet-gene interactions are strongly influenced by many environmental, socioeconomic and behavioral factors that can modify or enhance the effects of genetics. For this reason, dietary recommendations based on a person's genotype must be accompanied by long-term lifestyle changes (eg., regular exercise) to be most effective.

In closing, I would like to remind readers that nutrition has been, and will continue to be, the cornerstone of good health and disease prevention – and good nutrition is worth investing in. This is particularly true as new nutritional genetic tests come to market. Dietary interventions, including those using genetic tests, will play an important role in disease prevention and treatment, especially as populations around the world increase, grow older and become more obese.

As we learn more about health-promoting dietary components and how they interact with our genes – and incorporate this knowledge into our dietary choices – we should be able to achieve optimal health and well-being earlier and maintain it longer. This may be the single most important outcome to emerge from 100 years of nutrition research and the sequencing of the human genome. If the benefits of nutritional genomics can be delivered to the public at a price we can afford and in a manner we understand, this will truly be a grand achievement of science and technology.

Raymond L. Rodriguez, PhD, Director
Center of Excellence for Nutritional Genomics
University of California, Davis
Davis, California

From the Authors

Ruth DeBusk, PhD, RD and Yael Joffe, RD (SA)

We first thought of *It's Not Just Your Genes!* as a way to introduce you to the fascinating world of genomics. Genetic technologies are revolutionizing health care and, in order to take full advantage of the advances emerging from this field, we need to get comfortable with its language and concepts. Today we know that, rather than viewing our genetic make-up as a hand of cards that have already been dealt, we have the power to use the information encoded in our genes to help us make informed choices that will maximize our genetic potential. Reading our personal genetic "message" is like having access to a treasure map – one that can lead us to excellent health, into our golden years!

Nutritional genomics (nutrigenomics for short) is the new scientific discipline dedicated to unraveling the mystery of what it means – in genetic terms – to live well. Nutrition scientists, health care professionals and every one of us has a stake in the continuing development of this field, based on our common desire to translate genetic information into practical prescriptions for personalized health care. Nutrigenomics is a marathon not a sprint; while much is already known, the next stages of discovery will require patient, cooperative effort. But the search is on, and the excitement is palpable. A true adventure lies ahead!

Knowledge is power and, through this book, our goal is to empower you so that you can take control of your health and improve the quality of your life. With the advent of nutrigenomics, we envision healthier human beings who owe their vitality to a gene-smart lifestyle, enjoying life right up to the last minute and going out like a light bulb – having burned brightly to the very end. We truly believe that by applying the lessons encoded in your genes, you can improve your chances to live life to its fullest, for many years to come.

This book will provide you with a working familiarity of nutrigenomics and show you why it's so important. We'll tell you where things stand as well as the implications for the future. With the help of our editor Luba Vikhanski, we've done our best to make *It's Not Just Your Genes!* short, sweet and light as a garden salad. Don't skip the appetizing first chapter and go to the "main course" – you'll miss the structural framework that will help you gain a full understanding of the topics that are of special interest to you.

It's Not Just Your Genes! is not a magic bullet. Just reading it won't banish your health issues, make you lose weight or keep you forever young. Genetic risk is not absolute, and your individual genetic profile, along with how you choose to live, are major determinants of how your risk will play out in the long run. By gathering the information you need to make healthy choices, you have the power to optimize your individual potential. The era of personalized nutrition is upon us – join us on this fascinating journey into a new era and to a better life!

Biographies of the Authors

RUTH M. DEBUSK, PhD, RD

Dr. Ruth DeBusk has almost 40 years of experience in the combined fields of nutrition and genetics. She has served as a university professor and genetic researcher, as well as a registered dietitian in private practice working in the areas of genetics and nutrition. Dr. Ruth, as her students fondly called her, is the author of numerous scientific papers and four books, including *Genetics: The Nutrition Connection*, published by the American Dietetic Association for use in educating health care professionals about the upcoming era of nutritional genomics. She's a popular speaker, with a passion for educating professional and lay audiences about nutritional genomics.

On a personal note, Ruth's life at the moment can best be described as The Great Balancing Act: juggling seeing patients at her practice in Tallahassee, Florida, and keeping up with the latest in nutritional genomics; writing and speaking; working with American Dietetic Association members to develop a nutrigenomics practitioner career path; and working with the exceptionally talented people in the educational software company, Interactive Training Media, Inc. that she co-owns. Her family, friends, colleagues and Samoyed dogs help to make it all balance out in the face of great odds!

YAEL JOFFE, RD (SA)
South African-born Yael Joffe is a registered dietitian, licensed in South Africa and the United Kingdom, who specializes in nutrigenomics. Now based in the United States, Yael serves as Director of Diet and Nutrition for Sciona, Inc., a provider of nutrigenomics testing services in Boulder, Colorado. Yael collaborates with key academic partners from around the world and is actively involved in raising awareness about nutrigenomic applications and its promising future among both health practitioners – especially dietitians – and the general population. In addition to her activities in the private sector, Yael developed and supervises a nutrigenomics module that has been incorporated into the Masters in Nutrition degree offered by the University of Stellenbosch in South Africa. She is also conducting doctoral research on the genetics of obesity in black African women with the University of Cape Town, also in South Africa. A firm believer in the combined benefits of diet and exercise, Yael recently ran the New York marathon and celebrated her achievement with a genetically-appropriate macaroni and cheese dinner!

The authors share a common philosophy of empowering individuals to make educated decisions about their diet and health. This book is the product of that shared commitment.

Introduction

. . . .

Eating is one of life's great pleasures. In fact, humans indulge in eating more than just about any other pleasurable activity – enjoying a snack or meal an estimated 86,000 times over the course of a lifetime! With such frequent food consumption, making sure you eat right is vital for maintaining long-lasting health. But what's "right" depends a lot on who you are.

Some people have high blood pressure even when they totally banish salt from their diets, while others have normal blood pressure despite indulging in salty foods. Some people's cholesterol level soars from just looking at a layer cake, while others can eat it five times a week and stay healthy and thin. And speaking of weight, here's the kicker: even most popular "miracle" diets work only on certain people.

The secret behind all this dramatic variation can be summarized in one word: *genes.*

Each of us has a unique body chemistry determined by our genes – those tiny structures that serve as the blueprint for everything from our hair color to our susceptibility to disease. Genes also determine the way our body responds to food and physical activity. That's why in the long run, our diet and lifestyle must be tailored to our genes.

In this book, you'll learn about nutritional genomics – the emerging science of personalized, gene-smart nutrition. Thanks to our growing understanding of how genes influence our long-term health, it is now possible to live happier, fuller lives by choosing the right path – toward the diet and lifestyle decisions that make the most sense in terms of our specific genetic profiles.

1

Good genes and bad genes?

People sometimes think about genes as a jail sentence; they assume that whatever your genes "say" determines your fate for life. In fact, nothing could be further from the truth. While we all have a mixture of "good" and "bad" traits embedded in our genes, no genetic message is etched in stone. In many cases, we can modify these messages by making smart nutritional choices, and change our genetic destiny in the process.

It is possible to maximize your genetic potential. By living in harmony with your personal genetic profile, you can reach your highest possible level of intellectual and physical achievement. You can stay healthy and live longer. And while personalized nutrition can't promise that you'll never get sick, you can minimize your risk of disease by knowing your genetic susceptibilities and making the appropriate choices.

There's another good reason to adjust your diet to your genes: life is short. Wouldn't it be wonderful to just relax and enjoy what you eat, and not worry about nutritional warnings all day long? Armed with a clear understanding of your genetic make-up, you will be able to make positive decisions, based both on the "minus" column – areas you have to watch – and the "plus" column – areas where you have a leg up on the genetic competition. Knowing what really works for you is a powerful incentive because it takes the guesswork (and the despair!) out of healthy eating.

Nutritional genomics is a journey that has only recently begun, and much about the interplay among genes, diet and lifestyle remains to be discovered. But what's already known is so exciting that we invite you to join us on this journey. Part of this book is about now and how genetic science can already influence our daily lives. The rest of the book focuses on what can be expected in the future.

What's already certain, however, is that the genetic revolution has forever changed our world. Now, thanks to nutritional genomics, we can look inside ourselves in a way that was never possible before, and ask: how do our genes make us special? The answer to this question can put us all on the road to a better life, by allowing us to make personal, science-based decisions maximizing our potential for life-long health and well-being.

Chapter 1

Your Genes and Your Health

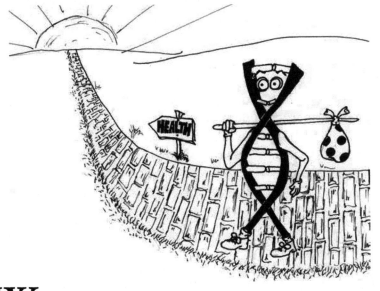

Whe all know them. First, there's the health-conscious executive who maintains a low-fat diet and works out regularly and is "rewarded" with a debilitating heart attack at the age of 40. On the other extreme, there's the elderly man who looks and feels terrific despite decades of smoking and a taste for all the wrong foods. Rather than railing against what seems like random injustice, take heart: there *is* a logical explanation coded into the genes of every individual person. And thanks to science's ability to crack this code, it is now possible to use genetic information for the betterment of our own health.

Take two famous examples. Running guru Jim Fixx quit smoking and shed 50 pounds soon after starting to jog at age 35. In 1977, he authored *The Complete Book of Running*, a best-seller that helped launch

America's fitness revolution. In 1984, Fixx died of a heart attack while running on a tree-shaded road in Vermont. He was 52. An autopsy revealed major blockage in his three main arteries.

Another example is Winston Churchill. This colorful statesman – best known for serving as the British Prime Minister during World War II – was grossly overweight and partial to bone marrow, whiskey and cigars. Despite this, he remained astonishingly vigorous, beginning his second term as Prime Minister at the age of 77 and maintaining an active schedule until his death in 1965 – 2 months after his much-celebrated 90th birthday. When asked to reveal the secret of his remarkably long and vibrant life, he answered in two words: "No sport."

The truth, of course, is that a reasonable level of exercise is good for the body and soul. But in order to promote health and vitality, one's exercise program, as well as other major lifestyle choices – first and foremost, nutritional choices – must be tailored to our genes. Genetic screening was not available in Jim Fixx's time, but considering that his cholesterol level was high, he may have been genetically predisposed to developing clogged arteries. Churchill, on the other hand, was obviously blessed with protective genes that allowed him to live a long and healthy life despite some very unhealthy lifestyle choices.

What does this mean for you? Most of us have a mixture of "Fixx" genes that make us susceptible to disease and "Churchill" genes that protect us from harm. By knowing where you stand on this genetic spectrum, you can adjust your diet and your lifestyle choices accordingly. Remember, while genes determine our vulnerabilities, it is our lifestyle – including the food we eat, the air we breathe and the toxic substances to which we are exposed – that determines to what extent these vulnerabilities will affect how well and how long we live.

Scientists all over the world are actively examining the interplay among genes, lifestyle and health. Their research is adding up to a vast reservoir of information from which we can carefully start drawing practical conclusions. Throughout this book, we'll be telling you about the latest advances in this area, and how they can help us make the most of our genetic inheritance.

But first, let's get down to basics – a few words about what genes are, how they were discovered and what role they play in health and disease.

Gene history in a nutshell

While people have long known that both human and animal offspring tend to resemble their parents, up until the late 19th century, how traits were passed down from one generation to the next was the focus of a lively intellectual debate. Some researchers claimed all the hereditary information was contained in the sperm, while others argued it was all in the egg. Among those who believed that both parents contributed traits to their children, some spoke of "hereditary fluids" that blended together, much like paint on an artist's palette.

It was a modest Augustinian monk, Gregor Mendel, who showed in the 1860s that traits were inherited in distinct units – now called "genes" – equally contributed by both parents. Inspired by his region's interest in better crops, as well as by an imperial order for monks to make themselves useful to society, he turned the garden next to his monastery – in what is now the Czech Republic – into an open-air horticultural laboratory and spent eight years breeding pea plants of different colors, sizes and shapes. After sorting and counting thousands of different hybrid pea plants, he revealed key laws governing inheritance and published his results in 1866.

Mendel's work was so far ahead of his time that it was misunderstood and ignored by his contemporaries. (It didn't help that Mendel, a humble cleric, had no formal standing in the scientific community.) However, when Mendel's work was rediscovered around 1900, well after his death, it laid the foundation for modern genetic science. Mendel was posthumously proclaimed the Father of Genetics, and his work with pea hybrids is considered among the most elegant experiments in the entire history of biology.

The word "gene," describing Mendel's units of heredity, was coined in 1909 by the Danish botanist Wilhelm Johannsen. It is derived from the Greek word *genos*, meaning "birth."

In the late 1900s, a prominent British physician named Archibald Garrod suggested that genetic defects might cause inherited diseases. He studied a rare disorder characterized by a rather harmless but peculiar symptom: the patient's urine turned dark when exposed to air. Initially, this disorder, dubbed alkaptonuria, was thought to result from bacterial infection, but Garrod suspected it was hereditary. In 1931, Garrod expanded on this theory in a book called *Inborn Factors in Disease*, in which he suggested that many serious disorders were caused by genes.

But what are genes made of? By around the middle of the 20th century, scientists were fairly sure that genes were stored in long molecules known as DNA (short for deoxyribonucleic acid) that are coiled inside the cell nucleus. However, how genes were stored, and how genetic information was copied and transmitted to the next generation, remained a mystery.

In 1953, answers to these questions began to emerge from a laboratory at the University of Cambridge. Two enterprising scientists – US-born James Watson and Englishman Francis Crick – figured out the "double-helix" structure of DNA. Relying largely on the work of Rosalind Franklin and that of other scientists, the two intuitively knew they were on to something big. In fact, after he and Watson made their discovery, Crick reportedly proclaimed in a Cambridge pub that they had "solved the secret of life."

The magnificent double helix

When Watson and Crick first showed their proposed DNA model to colleagues, the general reaction was that "the structure was too pretty not to be true." Now, with scientific hindsight we can confidently say that DNA is not only pretty, but is also a winner: virtually all organisms – bacteria, plants, yeast and animals, including humans – store their genetic information in the form of DNA.

The DNA is known as a double helix because it consists of two interconnected coils that together look like a corkscrew-shaped ladder. Each coil is made of structural units that come in four different forms, designated by the letters A, C, G and T. Human DNA has about three billion such genetic "letters"; it can be likened to a twisted rope ladder with three billion rungs (see Figure 1-1).

The "genetic letters" encode the basic information about how a human body functions and what it looks like. They form "sentences" that carry instructions for making proteins – the large, complex

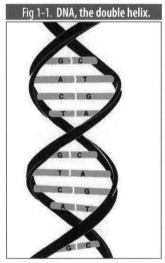

Fig 1-1. DNA, the double helix.

The four genetic "letters" of DNA are: A = adenine, C = cytosine, G = guanine, T = thymine.

molecules that regulate body functions and serve as building blocks for tissues. Each such "sentence" is a gene (see Figure 1-2).

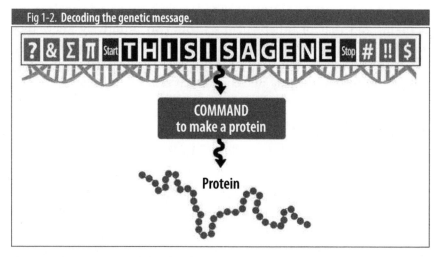

Fig 1-2. Decoding the genetic message.

Genes are "sentences" encoded within the DNA molecule. They contain instructions for making all the proteins that make our bodies function.

The instructions contained in the genes start making sense after being decoded – in other words, after they are transformed into working protein molecules. Just as the letters of our alphabet acquire a meaning only when combined in a certain fashion – for example, C, A and T form a meaningful word when put together in a particular order – so the genetic letters follow a certain order to create a functioning protein.

An average gene has about 3,000 genetic "letters," though some genes are significantly longer. Interestingly, much of the DNA does not code for proteins and has no known function. Often referred to as "junk DNA," it most likely contains information or provides a function we do not yet understand.

It was originally believed that humans had 100,000 genes, but as our knowledge has increased, this number has been gradually revised downwards. One of the latest estimates is that each person has only 20,000 to 25,000 genes. Coming up with an accurate number of genes is challenging because it's not always clear where one gene begins and another ends along the length of the complex DNA molecule.

In order to fit into the tiny nucleus of each cell, DNA is packed tightly into distinct storage units called chromosomes. Humans have 23 pairs of chromosomes; in each pair, one has been inherited from our mother and one from our father (see Figure 1-3).

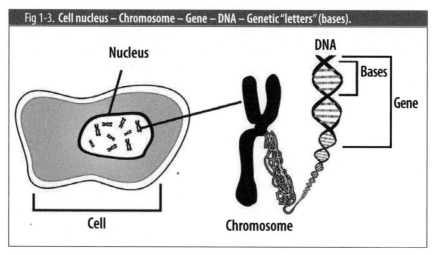

Fig 1-3. Cell nucleus – Chromosome – Gene – DNA – Genetic "letters" (bases).

Nucleus

DNA

Bases

Gene

Cell

Chromosome

Tightly packed into the nucleus of each human cell are 46 chromosomes. They contain the three billion genetic "letters" that make up the DNA molecule.

If you think of DNA as an encyclopedia, then a chromosome is one volume of that encyclopedia, and a gene is one sentence in that volume. Each gene carries a distinct message – a message that scientists all over the world are trying to read.

THE HUMAN GENOME PROJECT

An enormous boost to all genetic research has come from the Human Genome Project, launched in 1990. The Project is an ambitious international undertaking coordinated by the Department of Energy and the National Institutes of Health in the US. The main goal of the Project has been to "spell out" all three billion genetic letters of the human genome – the full set of genetic information that makes people what they are – as well as determining these letters' positions on the chromosomes and identifying all the genes. Completed in 2003, this part of the Human Genome Project gave scientists a priceless gift: a readable "directory" of human heredity.

While scientists involved in the Human Genome Project continue to pursue additional important objectives, thanks to their efforts the "secret of life" is now available to all; anyone can browse through the human genome on the Internet at no cost, or look it up in the library. Access to this information has enormously accelerated the pace of scientific progress in all gene-related research areas and has greatly improved our understanding of the interaction among genes, nutrition and lifestyle – in other words, nutritional genomics.

How we all differ

When scientists decipher the messages encoded in human genes, their research applies to all people because we all share the same basic set of genetic material. In fact, 99.9 percent of human DNA is identical in all of us. But hold on – isn't each person supposed to be genetically unique?

Each of us, indeed, is a unique genetic specimen. Despite the large amount of hereditary material we all share, we owe our uniqueness to the fact that DNA is such a long molecule: the 0.1 percent of DNA that differs from one person to another corresponds to 3 million genetic "letters". These letters – enough to create a virtually unlimited number of "word" combinations – account for the infinite diversity of human beings on the planet.

Amidst this diversity, however, it's possible to find many gene versions, or variants, that are shared by large numbers of people. For example, most people may have a G at a particular rung of the DNA ladder, while a certain percentage of the population might have a C in the same position.

The majority of these gene variants don't seem to negatively affect our health. They can be likened to alternative spellings of the same word that are both acceptable, such as "gray" and "grey." Sometimes, however, variations in the genes can affect the way the body functions. This would be akin to spelling mistakes that completely alter a word's meaning, for example, from "goat" to "coat" (see Figure 1-4).

Understanding your own gene variants gives you the power to maximize your health potential by adjusting your diet and lifestyle to your own unique set of genes. In this book, we'll be devoting special attention to the gene variants it pays to get to know – the ones that are known to alter your susceptibility to common, chronic diseases.

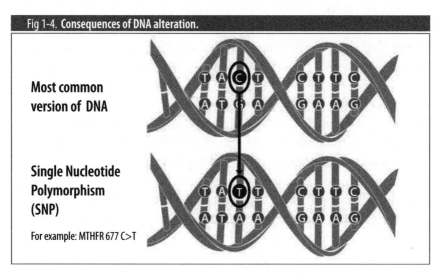

Fig 1-4. Consequences of DNA alteration.

Most common version of DNA

Single Nucleotide Polymorphism (SNP)

For example: MTHFR 677 C>T

Even a slight change in the genetic code, such as the replacement of one DNA "letter," can result in an altered protein that may work differently within the body.

The role of genes in disease

In one way or another, genes are involved in virtually all diseases. However, in some cases diseases result mainly from naturally occurring variations in a person's genetic material, with little influence from environmental factors. Examples of these types of disorders – which are usually caused by abnormalities in a single gene – are cystic fibrosis, Huntington's and Tay-Sachs disease.

In contrast, most common diseases arise from a combination of genetic and environmental influences, including diet and exposure to harmful toxins. Disorders of this type – called "complex diseases" because they are brought on by a variety of factors – include conditions such as heart disease and stroke, obesity, most cancers, mental illness, asthma, arthritis and diabetes, to name a few.

For the most part, even if you carry gene variants that mark you as being susceptible to a complex disease, the variants alone won't make you ill. They do, however, increase the risk that a disease will develop in the presence of certain behaviors. For example, two people may have the same gene variant that makes them genetically predisposed to diabetes. However, if one is overweight and the other isn't, the overweight individual runs a much greater risk of developing diabetes.

Conversely, some gene variants are protective, minimizing harmful influences and reducing our risk of disease. It is such protective variants that probably account for the stories of Churchill-esque individuals who reach a ripe old age despite breaking all the "rules" of good health. Such genetic protection, however, can never be regarded as absolute. Just like genetic susceptibility, it might offer protection only in the presence of positive choices relating to diet and lifestyle.

In summary, what's important from a practical standpoint is that most gene variants are not definitively good or bad. Their effects can be fine-tuned or even altered by appropriate lifestyle choices.

That's great news for all of us concerned with minimizing our risk of disease well in advance, before health problems get a chance to develop. It's empowering to know that we don't just "get" a disease and that our lifestyle choices go a long way towards determining whether genetic susceptibility becomes our destiny. Scientific knowledge can help us reduce our genetic vulnerabilities and reap full benefit from our positive genetic endowment. In this book, we'll provide you with guidelines for understanding your unique genetic make-up and for making gene-smart choices for better long-term health.

Chapter 2

Affecting Your Genes – For the Better

"Genes, like diamonds, are forever," to quote Richard Dawkins, noted geneticist and the author of a number of books on popular science. Indeed, good or bad, your genes and gene variants are with you for the rest of your life. If necessary, however, it is in your power to change your genetic destiny in many ways.

We are not talking about actually changing the genes themselves. That's the province of gene therapy, a complicated and still-experimental procedure that is undertaken only to treat severe disorders. What we have in mind is modifying your behavior so that your genetic message spells mostly good news.

It's Not Just Your Genes!

One strategy for staying healthy is to *avoid* potential triggers of diseases to which you are genetically susceptible. It's not always easy because you may be exposed to numerous triggers and your DNA may contain a number of predisposing genetic features. But when the condition is caused by a single genetic feature that can be turned "on" or "off" depending on environmental factors, simply avoiding the trigger can be remarkably effective.

The avoidance approach works well, for example, for lactose intolerance. This is a condition that can be caused by defects in the genetic mechanisms responsible for producing lactase – an enzyme that breaks down the milk sugar known as lactose. Individuals with this genetic defect cannot break down lactose so that it can be properly absorbed by the small intestine. Treatments are available, but the simplest solution is to avoid lactose-containing foods. Although the underlying genetic material has not been changed, the person's health and well-being is changed dramatically as a result of nutritional choices.

Another strategy is to *supplement* those substances that our body fails to produce because of genetic limitations. In fact, although we may not be aware of the gene-based nature of the problem, we all resort to this strategy every day.

For example, because we can't make vitamin C, we need to regularly eat foods that are rich sources of this vitamin, such as citrus fruits. The same holds for needing to eat certain building blocks of protein and adequate amounts of certain fats. This is because, over the course of evolution, we have become unable to produce critical enzymes needed for synthesizing these nutrients within the body itself. While we have long known that failure to get these nutrients through diet can lead to disease and even death and have discovered the foods we need to ensure an adequate supply, it is only recently that we have come to understand the genetic basis of the problem. Luckily, we can circumvent our gene-based nutritional deficiencies by supplementing our diet with the right foods.

Along with avoiding the trigger and supplementing our diet with those nutrients our body cannot adequately produce, there is a third, highly exciting way to optimize our genetic potential. Because scientists now understand how genes perform differently under different circumstances, it is actually possible to alter the way our genes work – "revving them up" to increase the potency of positive genetic factors and "gearing down" to minimize a gene's detrimental effects.

To understand how nutritional factors can influence this genetic "gearbox," we must first take a look at gene *expression* – the process by which information in our genes is translated into proteins. Proteins, the "worker" molecules that play an active role in bodily functions, can be produced in greater or smaller amounts because various factors can cause gene expression to be switched on or off. One of these factors is nutrition.

The nutrients we consume can change a gene's performance by acting on its "control" region. Unlike the rest of the gene, which contains coded instructions for making a protein molecule, the control region – where communication between the environment and the genetic material occurs – regulates the rate of protein synthesis (see Figure 2-1).

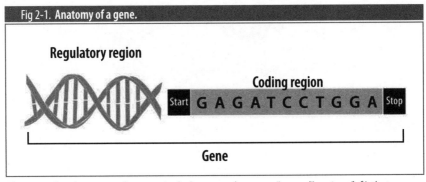

Fig 2-1. Anatomy of a gene.

Regulatory region

Coding region

Start G A G A T C C T G G A Stop

Gene

The typical architecture of a gene includes a regulatory or "control" region (left) that controls the way the gene works and a coding region (right) that contains instructions for making a protein.

It's Not Just Your Genes!

Some food ingredients produce their effects by directly hooking up with proteins that bind to the control region in DNA. Others act indirectly, by influencing the mechanisms that give the DNA its protein-producing instructions. Whatever their path, however, food ingredients can either accelerate or slow down the action of particular genes, causing these genes to produce proteins in greater or smaller amounts, which in turn affects how the body functions (see Figure 2-2).

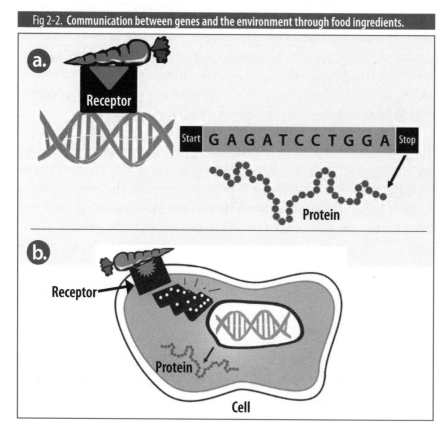

Fig 2-2. Communication between genes and the environment through food ingredients.

a. Food ingredients can directly affect the way genes work – by "docking" onto proteins that bind to the DNA, leading to an increase or decrease in gene expression.

b. Food ingredients can also affect genes indirectly – by "docking" onto proteins at the surface of cells. Such docking action sets off a chain reaction ("domino effect") that ultimately results in an increase or decrease in gene expression.

20

Here are a few examples of nutrients that stimulate higher levels of protein synthesis:

GLUCOSINOLATES –
found in vegetables such as broccoli, cauliflower and Brussels sprouts – activate the genes responsible for cleansing the body of toxins. If your toxin-removing genes are not working efficiently, including these ingredients in your diet is crucial for good health because they increase the rate of gene-based protein synthesis. And even if your toxin-removing genes are working properly, a nutritional boost may be needed if you are frequently exposed to environmental toxins or are taking several medications that may not be fully cleared from the body.

GENISTEIN –
(found in soy) activates a gene whose action increases the levels of HDL ("good") cholesterol.

RESVERATROL –
(in red wine) stimulates a gene that protects tissues against damage from destructive molecules called free radicals.

Some food ingredients are gene "silencers" – they slow down or stop protein synthesis altogether. The silencers include:

LYCOPENE –
(in tomato products) slows down a gene involved in prostate cancer.

GAMMA-LINOLENIC ACID –
(in evening primrose oil) reduces the activity of a gene involved in breast cancer and other malignant tumors.

CURCUMIN –
(in the spice turmeric) suppresses genes associated with inflammation.

It's Not Just Your Genes!

OMEGA-3 FATTY ACIDS –
(from cold-water fish and plant foods, such as flaxseed) also help "gear down" inflammation genes.

Obviously, turning genes on and off is infinitely more complex than simply flipping an electric switch. Genes are part of a living cell and interact with the environment and with each other in a multitude of ways not yet fully understood. However, thanks to scientific advances, we can already point to a number of mechanisms – like the examples given above – that play a crucial role in human health.

The bottom line is this: nutrition is arguably *the* most powerful tool we have for affecting the way our genes work. Progress in nutritional genomics – an emerging discipline that uses genetic data to define personalized, science-based strategies for meeting our nutritional needs – is so rapid that new studies are coming out regularly and new aspects of the interplay among genes, diet and lifestyle are continuously being discovered.

What's already obvious, however, is that no diet or lifestyle is optimal for everyone. One-size-fits-all is out; personalized nutrition is in. In the next chapter, we'll start considering healthy habits that are designed specially for you.

Chapter 3

Heart Health

"Gene card, please."

Paul and Jennifer, a happily married couple in their early 30s, have a lot in common. Unfortunately, among the many things they share is a family history of heart disease; both have had close relatives who died relatively early from heart disease. That's why they took time off today to get a check-up at a clinic that specializes in the new science of nutritional genomics. They want to increase their chances of living long and healthy lives together and have heard that these days the "in" thing is personalized nutrition advice based on genes.

It's Not Just Your Genes!

Since Paul and Jennifer share similar health concerns, they assume that they will leave the clinic with a single set of recommendations. But as the nutritional genomics practitioner swipes their cards to examine their genetic profiles, they discover that personalized nutrition means just that — each of them is going to get personal advice, and the recommendations will not necessarily be the same.

Paul's cholesterol is really high. An avid runner, he is worried about his arteries clogging up but is also reluctant to start taking cholesterol-lowering drugs. The nutritional genomics practitioner has some food for thought: Paul's genetic profile indicates that he is likely to respond well to a diet low in saturated fats and cholesterol. He decides to try this for 3 months to see if his levels of "bad" cholesterol drop.

Paul also gets some delicious good news. He had assumed that, to lower his risk of developing high blood pressure, his regular indulgence in salty snacks would become a thing of the past. However, Paul's genetic screening does not indicate that such a change is necessary. Paul breathes a sigh of relief: if he has to cut saturated fats from his diet, he can still indulge in his beloved salted popcorn.

Jennifer's genes reveal another story altogether. Unlike her husband, she is susceptible to developing high blood pressure upon eating high salt foods and is advised to make reducing her overall salt intake a high priority. Her genetic profile also suggests that she should eat more anti-inflammatory foods as well as foods rich in B vitamins, particularly folate.

The other thing Jennifer discovers is that she needs to make every effort to kick her smoking habit. Although Paul — with the backing of the US Surgeon General — has been urging her to quit for years, it wasn't until she found out that her genes put her at an especially high risk for accumulating toxins that she realized the time had come to take the problem seriously. Looking into her husband's eyes, she resolves to put down the smokes — for good.

Finally, she is told that she should get serious about exercise; her genes reveal that she's particularly susceptible to the ill effects of a sedentary lifestyle on her heart. Paul would love his wife to go jogging with him, and with the scientific back-up provided by genetic screening, Jennifer finally decides to take the first step.

Gene cards do not yet exist. However, the imaginary scenario above illustrates the new, gene-smart approach to making optimal dietary choices. Getting beyond the "one-size-fits-all" mantra for heart health, new genetic screening techniques are creating an innovative way of preventing disease, in which the most appropriate recipe for heart and circulatory system health is encoded on a case-by-case basis, right in your genes!

In this chapter, we'll focus on several areas in which healthy heart practices vary considerably based on an individual's genetic profile. We'll be talking about developing a strong circulatory system in which a healthy heart pumps blood through unclogged blood vessels so that oxygen and nutrients can be delivered to body cells, while metabolic waste products are efficiently removed. Considering that cardiovascular disease, which includes heart disease, stroke and impaired circulation in general, is the leading cause of death and illness in the United States, reducing its risk with your genetic profile in mind can go a long way towards helping you live longer and stronger, and enjoying more precious years with the ones you love.

Getting your fats straight

In the early 20th century, heart disease was so rare doctors reported treating on average only one case a month, even in large city hospitals. The staggering increase in heart disease since the mid-20th century is the legacy of changes in diet and lifestyle that have occurred throughout Western civilization since the dawn of the industrial era.

Deep within our genetic code, we still carry the genes of our ancient hunter-gatherer ancestors, and – surprise! – these genes are at odds with the muffins, pizzas and ice cream that dominate the typical Western diet. Incidences of cardiovascular disease and other major "diseases of civilization" have soared, apparently due to a collision between the human genome – still programmed to survive Stone Age-style deprivations – and the overstuffed affluence of modern society.

Among the numerous dietary ingredients to which our genes are poorly adapted are processed foods and refined sugars. However, in terms of heart disease, the prime suspect on the crime scene has been fat. Eating large amounts of certain fats – particularly saturated fats, found mainly in processed foods and

HEART NUMBERS	
1 million	Amount of blood pumped by the heart in an average lifetime, in barrels
3 million	Number of times the human heart beats in 1 year
2.5 billion	Approximate number of times the heart of a 70-year-old has beaten
60,000	Length of all blood vessels stretched end to end, in miles
64 million	Number of Americans with cardiovascular disease, including stroke
50 million	Number of Americans with high blood pressure (approximately 20% of the population)
Close to 1 million	Number of people dying annually of cardiovascular disease, including stroke, in the United States (approximately 35% of all deaths)
12 million	Number of people dying annually of cardiovascular disease, including stroke, around the world
$500 billion	Annual economic cost of cardiovascular disease, including stroke, to the United States (including direct medical costs and lost productivity)

such animal foods as cream, whole milk and fatty meats – raises the blood level of cholesterol. And when there is an excess of cholesterol in the body, it is deposited in arteries, including the coronary arteries that lead to the heart.

It's important to keep in mind that there are two types of cholesterol: LDL, the "bad" cholesterol, is the villain that clogs arteries. The other type, HDL or "good" cholesterol, actually protects us against cardiovascular disease. Ideally, we should adopt a lifestyle that promotes keeping the LDL cholesterol low and the HDL cholesterol high. However, there are striking differences in the way people respond to dietary measures aimed at achieving these goals. Several hundred genes are thought to be involved in the processing of fat and cholesterol by the body, and their effects can be fairly dramatic.

Take, for example, the relationship between dietary fat and (the "good") HDL cholesterol. Studies show that eating polyunsaturated fats – the ones that occur in vegetable oils and fatty fish – can have diametrically opposed effects, depending on your genes.

Here's how it works: a gene called APOA1 (pronounced "ā-pō-ā-one") is involved in regulating the body's production of HDL cholesterol. In about 30 percent of people, however, there's a variation in the control region of this gene: one of the genetic "letter" Gs has been replaced with the genetic "letter" A. When people with the A version of the gene consume a high percentage of polyunsaturated fats in their diet, their HDL cholesterol goes up. In contrast, in people with the more common G version, the *opposite* happens: their HDL cholesterol drops, even if their intake of polyunsaturated fat is exactly the same as the individual with the A version.

Scientists believe that polyunsaturated fat acts as a control switch for the APOA1 gene: depending on the gene version, the switch can turn HDL cholesterol production up or down. If these results are supported by further studies, people with the A version of the APOA1 gene will be able to reduce their risk of coronary heart disease by increasing the proportion of polyunsaturated fats in their diet and thereby directly raising their HDL – "good" – cholesterol levels.

Other genes may help explain the wildly differing results experienced by people who decide to follow the advice of the American government and adopt a diet that is low in cholesterol and saturated fat. While this prescription is designed to lower levels of the "bad" LDL cholesterol throughout the population, some people seem to reap the benefits while others watch their LDL cholesterol level remain the same even when they follow a strict diet. Similarly, some people can get away with eating all the saturated fat-laden bacon and sausage they like without dangerously raising their cholesterol; others see their cholesterol levels soar in response to a diet that includes even a moderate amount of these fatty foods.

These differences may be partly due to variants of another gene, called APOE ("ā-pō-ee"), which plays an important role in regulating cholesterol. It comes in three major versions, referred to as E2, E3 and E4, with the majority of people having the E3 version. People with the E4 variant, which occurs in 15 to 30 percent of the US population, tend to have higher total cholesterol levels. They are also particularly susceptible to the harmful effects of smoking and have an increased risk of diabetes when they are overweight. In addition, this gene variant appears to reverse the usual protective effects of moderate drinking.

On the other hand, E4 has one major advantage: this gene variant is particularly responsive to diet and lifestyle modifications. Apparently, it is people with E4 – and not those with E2 and E3 – who can most effectively lower their LDL ("bad") cholesterol if they go on a diet low in saturated fat. And if they also lose weight, take up exercise and give up smoking and drinking, they can greatly reduce their genetic predisposition to cardiovascular disease.

The benefit of knowing whether you have the E4 version of the APOE gene would seem to be obvious, but a word of caution is in order. E4 has yet another, less fortunate connection: this version of the gene is also associated with an increased risk of Alzheimer's disease. Of course not everyone with Alzheimer's has E4 nor does every E4 carrier develop Alzheimer's. There continues to be scientific debate concerning the association between Alzheimer's and APOE 4. Furthermore, promising research suggests that future nutritional interventions may help decrease Alzheimer's risk.

In any event, the APOE gene offers an excellent proof of principle: one fat doesn't fit all. In order to protect yourself from heart disease, the quantity and quality of fats in your diet must be adjusted according to your specific genetic profile.

Inflammation, heart attack and stroke

Monitoring your blood cholesterol is a prudent strategy if you want to avoid cardiovascular disease, but it's important to remember that cholesterol measurements often miss people at risk. About half of heart attacks and other cardiovascular problems occur in people with perfectly normal cholesterol levels. One of the "red flags" that may help identify these hidden candidates for heart disease is inflammation – the body's response to a potential threat.

No longer thought to be just a "plumbing" problem, today doctors recognize that clogging of the arteries is a complex process involving numerous factors, with one major component appearing to be chronic inflammation. Responding to a bacterial infection or oxygen-damaged LDL cholesterol (oxidative stress), the body's immune system releases a host of inflammatory substances, including molecules called cytokines and white blood cells that rush to the injury site to eliminate the threat and repair the damage. However, if this process is not properly controlled, it may result in chronic inflammation and damage to the body. This can happen, for example, if inflammatory genes fail to switch off after the threat is gone and get stuck in the "on" position, continuing to produce inflammatory substances when they are no longer needed.

Recognizing the multi-faceted nature of inflammation and the importance of its role in the development of heart disease, medical science is now developing an entirely new way of evaluating the impact of medications used to protect at-risk individuals. Cholesterol-lowering drugs known as statins may offer extra protection because, in addition to their effect on cholesterol, they are also believed to fight inflammation. And the beneficial effect of aspirin in reducing the risk of heart disease is now thought to be partly due to aspirin's anti-inflammatory action, not just its moderating effect on the formation of blood clots.

How can you tell if you have chronic inflammation? Medical science has not yet settled on a standard test, but a great deal of research focuses on C-reactive protein (CRP), a substance that indicates that inflammation is occurring in the body. It appears that high CRP levels can predict future heart disease as reliably as high cholesterol levels.

Your genes are another potential source of information. A key gene involved in the inflammatory response is interleukin-6 (IL6); among its functions, this gene stimulates the production of CRP. One of the variants of the IL6 gene, referred to as -174G>C ("minus 174 G-to-C," indicating the change from "letter" G to C has occurred in the control region of the gene, at letter position number 174), has been linked to an increased risk of coronary heart disease. People with this gene variant, who make up about 15 percent of the tested population, probably make more substances associated with inflammation, including CRP. Cigarette smoke, which stimulates the IL6 gene, exerts a particularly strong effect on this risky IL6 version, which means that people with this gene variant must be doubly careful to refrain from both active and passive smoking.

Another set of genes important in the inflammatory response is the interleukin-1 (IL1) family. These genes are "early responders" to infectious organisms and other threatening situations, and they orchestrate the body's reaction, which involves sounding the alarm by means of chemical messengers to "send in the cavalry" and then coordinating the battle plan. Variants of the IL1 genes can result in this response being stuck in the "on" position and making an individual susceptible to a host of inflammatory disorders.

It is important to note that, while nutritional genomics can be put to work to help people avoid the dangers of inflammation, not all inflammation is bad. Inflammation is an important part of the body's response to injury and invasion by infectious organisms. In fact, it's quite possible that high levels of inflammation offer an advantage early in life, providing protection

FACTORS THAT INCREASE THE RISK OF CARDIOVASCULAR DISEASE

▸ **Age**
Over 83 percent of people who die of coronary heart disease are 65 or older.

▸ **Gender**
Men have a greater risk of heart attack and stroke than do women, and their heart attacks tend to occur earlier in life. Although still not quite so high as for men, the risk for women does increase after menopause.

▸ **Strong family history of cardiovascular disease**

▸ **Genetic screening**
Did genetic screening reveal that you have gene variants associated with increased cardiovascular risk?

▸ **Obesity**

▸ **Diabetes**
Particularly type 2 diabetes when accompanied with obesity.

▸ **Cholesterol**
High LDL ("bad") cholesterol and low HDL ("good") cholesterol.

▸ **Chronic inflammation**

▸ **High blood pressure**

▸ **Smoking**

▸ **Sedentary lifestyle**

against childhood infections. Moreover, in both children and adults, a heightened inflammatory response might have provided an evolutionary advantage before the advent of antibiotics, when infection rather than cardiovascular disease was a major threat to survival. Today however, particularly among the elderly, chronic inflammation has few "up" sides and is believed to contribute to diseases including rheumatoid arthritis and inflammatory bowel disorders, such as Crohn's disease and ulcerative colitis. It is also implicated in conditions not traditionally linked to inflammation including heart attacks, type 2 diabetes, obesity, osteoporosis, gum disease and even some neurological disorders.

Identifying people with a genetic predisposition to chronic inflammation makes it possible to take early preventive action. And by making specific changes in their diets, these people will be able to benefit from nutrients known to have anti-inflammatory properties, such as the omega-3 fatty acids present in certain types of unsaturated fats, particularly in fish oil, as well as in certain plant oils and other foods (see text box "Anti-inflammatory food fight," p. 45).

Incidentally, the beneficial fatty acids mentioned above are thought to be responsible for the unusually low incidence of heart disease among the Greenland Eskimos. Apparently, although they historically enjoyed a high-fat diet, the fish providing much of their dietary protein had just the type of fat that's needed to keep inflammation on ice.

B vitamins: simple and safe

Just when you thought you'd gotten cholesterol and chronic inflammation under control, along comes a new culprit for cardiovascular disease – homocysteine.

"Homo-who?"

(An important aside to science-shy readers: if you feel you are losing track of all the blood tests you need to perform and all the foods you need to eat to

reduce your risk of cardiovascular disease, don't worry! The beauty of gene-based nutrition is in its simplicity – genetic screening reduces the confusion by identifying exactly which nutrition and lifestyle choices are most important for you. Now, back to our story...)

Homocysteine is an amino acid produced during the process of making certain proteins. When inefficiently metabolized in the body, homocysteine can build up to dangerously high levels, increasing the risk of heart disease, life-threatening blood clots and stroke. High levels of this compound are also associated with abnormal formation of the nervous system in the developing fetus.

Luckily, there is a simple, nutrition-based solution to the homocysteine problem. Homocysteine is converted to another substance by a process that involves the B vitamin folate, more commonly known as folic acid. Found in liver, leafy vegetables and other foods, folic acid – along with the vitamins B12, B6 and B2 – helps convert homocysteine to the next step in the metabolic chain of events, thereby preventing it from reaching high levels.

A safe and simple strategy for lowering the risk of heart disease is, therefore, to consume adequate levels of B vitamins, particularly folate, in order to keep homocysteine levels low. But while everyone can benefit from this advice, individuals who have undergone genetic screening can take this preventive nutrition one step further. This is because they can adjust their diet to their particular version of the gene called MTHFR, which plays an important role in the homocysteine conversion processes.

MTHFR codes for an enzyme that helps folate carry out its homocysteine-busting mission, with the tongue-twisting name of methylene-tetrahydrofolate reductase—we prefer M-T-H-F-R, for short. A substantial proportion of the population has a variant of MTHFR called 677C>T (the C letter has been replaced with a T at position 677 along the gene). This change makes the resulting enzyme partially defective and substantially reduces its efficiency in converting homocysteine to a less harmful molecule. This variation is apparently linked to geography; studies have shown that about half of Caucasians and Asians have one copy of the 677C>T variant, and about 12 percent of them have two copies of this variant. In this latter group in particular, MTHFR's activity is dramatically reduced. As a result, homocysteine builds up in the bloodstream.

People who have the 677C>T variant of the MTHFR gene need extra folate – from dietary sources and perhaps from a dietary supplement – to promote proper homocysteine conversion. Research has shown that when such individuals have a diet low in folate, their homocysteine levels rise sharply, but by increasing their intake of folate these levels can easily be brought down to normal.

B VITAMINS

The B vitamins – or the B vitamin complex – are a group of 11 compounds that perform a number of functions essential for our heart's continued well-being. Below are major food sources for four particularly important B vitamins: folate, B2, B6 and B12.

▸ **Folate** (in its synthetic form, folic acid)
Folate helps reduce the risk of cardiovascular disease. It is also necessary for normal fetal development and absolutely essential for developing new cells.

When looking for sources of folate, think foliage, as in leafy green. Excellent sources are fresh dark-green leafy vegetables such as spinach, as well as collard, mustard and turnip greens. Broccoli and asparagus are rich in folate. Other first-rate sources are lean beef, liver, mushrooms, oranges and orange juice, peanuts, dried beans, dried peas, such as blackeyed peas, potatoes, wheat germ and white beans and lentils. In the US, all grain and cereal products are fortified with folic acid.

••• *continued* •••

B VITAMINS *(continued)*

▶ **Vitamin B2**
Also called riboflavin, this vitamin is found in a variety of foods including animal products such as cheese, egg yolks, milk and yogurt, as well as beef, fish, liver, pork and poultry. Other sources of vitamin B2 are whole grains, such as brown rice, wheat germ and whole wheat; enriched grains, such as breads and cereals; and green vegetables, such as asparagus, broccoli, Brussels sprouts, spinach and many leafy greens.

▶ **Vitamin B6**
This vitamin, also called pyridoxine, is found mainly in unprocessed food. Avocados, bananas, broccoli, Brussels sprouts, dried beans and peas, eggs, kidneys, liver, pork, potatoes, poultry, spinach, sunflower seeds, sweet potatoes, walnuts, wheat germ and whole grains are all excellent sources.

▶ **Vitamin B12**
Vitamin B12, also called cobalamin, is found exclusively in animal foods. Good sources include: dairy products, eggs, fish and shellfish, organ meats such as liver and kidneys, red meat and poultry. Vegan sources include: fortified soymilk, margarine, soy powder, soy crumbles and chunks and yeast extracts.

Heart health issues aside, women considering having children, regardless of their genetic profiles, are advised to get at least 400 micrograms of folic acid each day from food or a dietary supplement or both, because this vitamin lowers the risk of nervous system defects in the fetus (called "neural tube defects").

Who needs a low-salt diet?

Salt – the "universal condiment" – was once far more than a humble shaker on the dinner table. Centuries ago in Africa, giant camel caravans carried salt from mid-Saharan marshes to the fabled city of Timbuktu, and children were known to be sold into slavery in exchange for a bit of the precious cargo.

Today salt has lost much of its mystique, but it's still a vital food ingredient. As any French fry fancier or pickle aficionado will tell you, it brings out flavor and adds pleasure to our meals. Yet nutrition warnings link excessive salt intake to a variety of ills. The National Heart, Lung, and Blood Institute and other health agencies strongly recommend a reduced-salt diet as a means of lowering blood pressure and keeping it within the normal range. Despite across-the-board admonitions about this mineral's potential dangers, is it really necessary for everyone to adopt a low-salt diet?

High blood pressure, or hypertension – the leading cause of strokes and a major risk factor for heart attacks – is no doubt a formidable foe. Preventing or lowering high blood pressure as soon as it is detected – before it causes damage to the blood vessels, heart, brain and other organs – is one of the most important aspects

FACTORS THAT INCREASE THE RISK OF HIGH BLOOD PRESSURE

▶ **Ethnicity**
High blood pressure tends to affect African Americans with greater frequency, at a younger age and with greater severity than Caucasians.

▶ **Age**
The risk of high blood pressure increases with age. Men tend to develop it most often between age 35 and 55, and women after menopause.

▶ **Family history**
Having a parent or other close relative with high blood pressure increases your risk.

▶ **Genetic screening**
Did genetic screening reveal that you have gene variants associated with increased risk for high blood pressure?

▶ **Obesity**

▶ **Alcohol**
Regularly drinking more than moderate amounts of alcohol (see text box "What is moderate drinking?" p. 37).

▶ **Sedentary lifestyle**

▶ **Salt**
Eating too much salt (for people with specific gene variants).

of maintaining cardiovascular health. But in more than 90 percent of cases, the reason for high blood pressure is unknown.

WHAT IS MODERATE DRINKING?

▸ Moderate drinking is defined by the Centers for Disease Control and Prevention as no more than 1 drink per day for women and 2 for men, on average.

▸ A drink is 12 ounces of beer, 5 ounces of wine or 1 1/2 ounces of distilled spirits.

▸ Each of the above drinks is the equivalent of 1/2 ounce of alcohol.

Salt is involved in the intricate body system that regulates blood pressure, and therefore is an obvious target in the battle against hypertension. Salt restriction, however, does not always reduce high blood pressure. In fact, while it works for some people, dietitians have long known that for a significant number of others, cutting back on salt has little or no effect.

As you may have already guessed, the reason for this discrepancy is believed to be genetic. People who have certain gene variants are "salt-sensitive"; when they eat a diet with a generous amount of salt, their blood pressure skyrockets. When they cut their salt intake, their blood pressure drops. In contrast, people who do not have these gene variants can pile on salt or shun it completely with little, if any, change in their blood pressure.

There are probably a number of genes that account for salt sensitivity. One of the prime suspects is the gene that codes for angiotensinogen, a protein that results in the formation of angiotensin II, which narrows the small blood vessels in tissues and causes blood pressure to rise. A variant of the angiotensinogen gene (AGT) – in which the genetic "letter" G in a particular position of the gene has been replaced by an A – appears to be at least partly responsible for salt sensitivity. This AGT variant is -6G>A. In one large study in the United States, 1,500 subjects were evaluated over a 3-year period. Those who had inherited the A gene variant from both parents had the greatest risk of developing high blood pressure, but when they reduced their salt intake, their blood pressure dropped. In contrast, people who had inherited 2 copies of the G version showed no reductions in blood pressure despite a low-salt diet. The G version is the "normal," more common version.

This study also revealed an interesting connection between salt, blood pressure and body weight. Subjects whose blood pressure was responsive to salt restriction also saw their blood pressure drop when they lost weight. On the other hand, weight loss had no effect on subjects lacking the salt-sensitivity variant; even if they shed pounds, their blood pressure stayed the same.

The important point here is that dietary approaches to the control of high blood pressure may only be effective if they match the gene variants you have. If you have the angiotensinogen gene variant that conveys salt-sensitivity, you must pay special attention to keeping your salt intake low in order to keep your blood pressure within the healthy range. You can also help control your blood pressure by keeping your weight down. If you have high blood pressure but do not have this variant, gene-smart health care providers now recognize that medication – not diet – may be the best first line of defense.

Maintaining your heart health the gene-smart way

Cardiovascular disease is such a complex disorder that preventing it requires action on several fronts, but thanks to nutritional genomics, it is now possible to design a custom-fitted strategy. Beginning with recommendations for the prevention of heart disease within the general population, we can then set priorities for a personalized heart health program, according to the genetic profile of the individual.

PHYSICAL ACTIVITY

A sedentary lifestyle increases the risk of cardiovascular disease. Yet more than 60 percent of Americans don't get enough exercise. Approximately 250,000 deaths per year in the United States – about 12 percent of total deaths – are due to a lack of regular physical activity.

Exercise doesn't need to be strenuous to bring health benefits. Even low-to-moderate physical activity for as little as 30 minutes a day is beneficial, ideally building up to 45 minutes to an hour 5 days a week. Walking, climbing stairs, yard work, moderate-to-heavy housework, dancing and home exercise – all count. Even better for improving cardiovascular fitness is vigorous aerobic exercise, such as brisk walking, running, swimming, cycling, roller-blading, and jumping rope (see boxes "Exercise advice" p.132 and "Tips to keep you exercising," p. 135).

SMOKING

Smoking is a major risk factor for developing cardiovascular disease, as well as many other disorders including cancer. While smoking is bad for everyone, for people whose genes make them particularly vulnerable to the harmful substances in cigarette smoke, it is literally lethal.

OBESITY

Being overweight not only increases the risk of heart disease, high blood pressure and stroke, it also contributes to the likelihood of developing diabetes and certain cancers. A person's tendency to become obese is greatly influenced by genetic factors, and weight loss programs should ideally be matched to each individual's genetic make-up. (See chapter 7 for definitions of healthy weight, overweight and obesity and a discussion of research on genes and body weight.)

FAT AND CHOLESTEROL

Regardless of your genetic make-up, it's important to keep your fat consumption within the range recommended for the general population – 20 to 35 percent of all calories. The way you choose to trim the fat, however, should be linked to your genetic profile. You may have to pay special attention to lowering the amount of saturated fat and cholesterol you consume, or, alternatively, to *increasing* the percentage of polyunsaturated fat in your diet (see text box "Know your fats!" below).

KNOW YOUR FATS!

Fats and cholesterol are certainly factors in heart disease. However, they get so much bad press it's easy to overlook all the good things they do: by supplying the essential fatty acids that the body itself cannot produce, fats help the body build up tissues and store energy. They're also important to communication between cells and are critical in our ability to absorb fat-soluble vitamins and other key nutrients.

So what's all this "saturation" stuff? Here's the scoop:

Fats are divided into two main groups depending on the predominant type of fatty acids they contain. "Saturated" fats are saturated — or full — of hydrogen atoms. "Unsaturated" fats are not. This chemical distinction plays a big role in how saturated and unsaturated fats look — and how they work in our bodies. As a rule saturated fats are solid at room temperature and unsaturated fats, liquid. When incorporated into cell membranes, the solid, rigid saturated fats make the cell stiff and creaky, preventing it from communicating effectively with its environment and with other cells. In contrast, the fluid unsaturated fats make the cell membrane flexible, allowing it to more easily change its shape in order to interact with the environment that surrounds it.

Below is a list of major food sources for different types of fat.

▸ **Cholesterol**
   is a form of fat found in animal foods such as egg yolks; dairy products (for example, butter, cream, ice cream, whole milk, yogurt); lard; liver and other organ meats; some shellfish; and beef, chicken, lamb, pork and turkey. Vegetable oils and shortenings are cholesterol-free.

••• *continued* •••

KNOW YOUR FATS! *(continued)*

▸ **Saturated fats**
are found mainly in animal products, and they are usually solid at room temperature. Foods high in saturated fats include high-fat dairy products (such as butter, cream, most cheeses, regular ice cream and whole milk); fatty, fresh and processed meats; lard; and the skin and fat of poultry. Palm oil and coconut oil also contain saturated fat.

▸ **Trans fatty acids**
are to be avoided. Period. Trans fatty acids are vegetable oils that have been processed and therefore contain more hydrogen, which causes them to behave like saturated fats. They are found in prepared foods containing partially hydrogenated oils. The most prominent examples of foods rich in trans fatty acids are most solid (stick) margarines and other solid vegetable shortenings, cookies, crackers and other baked goods and the fried foods served by many restaurants and fast-food chains.

▸ **Unsaturated fats**
are liquid at room temperature. They come in two types:

✓ **Polyunsaturated fats**
(often called PUFA, pronounced "poo-fa") have the lowest level of hydrogenation of all fat sources. They are found in different types of oil including canola, corn, cottonseed, fish, flaxseed, safflower, soy, sunflower and walnut oils.

✓ **Monounsaturated fats**
(often called MUFA, pronounced "moo-fa") are less hydrogenated than saturated fats but more hydrogenated than the polyunsaturated fats described above. Monounsaturated fats are the oils in olives, avocados and peanuts.

If you are advised to eat more polyunsaturated fats, you can avoid gaining weight by making sure to increase the *proportion* of these fats in your diet, rather than increasing the total amount of fat you consume. Moreover, because polyunsaturated fats tend to raise the *amount* of free radicals in the body, you must also take care to eat more antioxidants to offset this effect. (See chapter 4 for a discussion of antioxidants and lists of antioxidant-rich foods.)

••• *continued* •••

KNOW YOUR FATS! *(continued)*

▶ **Omega-3 and omega-6 fatty acids**
Compared with what we eat today, the diet of our ancient ancestors contained a much higher proportion of omega-3 than omega-6 fatty acids. This relative decline might be partly responsible for the current rise in cardiovascular disease and other chronic disorders. Consuming these beneficial fatty acids in adequate amounts is particularly important if your genes put you at risk for chronic inflammation.

While it's generally recommended that fish containing omega-3 fats be eaten twice a week, people with certain genetic profiles may be advised to eat a higher proportion of their fats as omega-3s. This may mean eating more than 2 fish or other omega-3-rich meals per week or including dietary supplements of high quality omega-3 fats, or both (see text box "Anti-inflammatory food fight," p. 45).

Another important way to decrease the inflammatory response could be described as BYOB – "Balance Your Omega Budget." By reducing your intake of omega-6 fats while at the same time increasing the amount of omega-3s, you can significantly help your body fight chronic inflammation, which is a significant risk factor for heart health.

The tricky part is to keep your total fat calories the same, regardless of whether they're coming from omega-3s or -6s. Therefore, it would be helpful to take a 2-pronged approach; try substituting an omega-3 oil for an omega-6 oil you commonly use *and* selecting omega-3-rich choices when deciding what kinds of protein you'll eat each day.

Remember, omega-6s are found in all animal fats, as well as vegetable oils such as corn oil, cottonseed oil, safflower oil, sesame seed oil and sunflower seed oil. Instead of salad dressings made from corn oil, choose those based on canola oil, or make your own using canola or walnut oil. In place of corn oil, butter or margarine in cooking, use canola or olive oil. (Olive oil is a monounsaturated fat that does not have any harmful effects on heart health and is likely beneficial.) Because processed food and baked goods often contain high percentages of omega-6 fats and trans fatty acids, decreasing consumption of these items will considerably help your overall health – and your budget.

For a sample menu balancing omega-6s and omega-3s over the course of a day's eating, see text box "BYOB-Balance your omega budget," p. 43.

BYOB – BALANCE YOUR OMEGA BUDGET

The goal here is to reduce the amount of omega-6 fats you consume while increasing the amount of omega-3 fats. The tricky part is to keep your total fat calories the same, regardless of whether they're coming from omega-3s or -6s, so it's helpful to think in terms of substituting an omega-3 oil for an omega-6 oil you commonly use *and* selecting omega-3-rich choices when deciding what kinds of protein you'll eat each day.

Remember, omega-6s are in all animal fats and vegetable oils such as corn oil, cottonseed oil, safflower oil, sunflower seed oil and sesame seed oil.

Good choices of omega-3s include fatty fish and fish oils, canola oil, flaxseed and flaxseed oil, walnuts and walnut oil, pumpkin seeds and, to some extent, soy oil (a mix of omega-6s and omega-3s).

To give you an idea of what a good balance between omega-6s and omega-3s looks like in terms of a day's eating, we've provided a sample menu based on approximately 1500 calories/day. A variety of recipes incorporating plant and animal sources of omega-3s can be found in the appendices.

Breakfast	• 1 cup nonfat yogurt sprinkled with ¼ cup granola • 4-5 walnuts • 3/4 cup mixed berries • 1 cup skim milk or nonfat, calcium-enriched soy or rice milk
Lunch	• 2 cups salad Nicoise made with boiled egg, fresh tuna, green beans, and canola vinaigrette • Slice of flaxseed bread • 1 medium fresh fruit of choice • Hot or cold unsweetened tea or other low-calorie beverage
Snack	• Low-fat yogurt or yogurt smoothie
Dinner	• 3 oz. chargrilled chicken breast • 1 cup steamed broccoli, tossed with olive oil and roasted, salted pumpkin seeds • 2 cups spinach salad with 2 tablespoons reduced calorie dressing • 1 cup skim milk or nonfat, calcium-enriched soy, rice or nut milk
Snack	• 2 medium wholegrain cookies • ½ large grapefruit or 1 medium orange

B VITAMINS

Most people have heard that women of childbearing age are advised to take folic acid during pregnancy in order to prevent brain-related birth defects. However, people may not be as aware that an adequate intake of folate and other B vitamins also reduces the risk of cardiovascular disease. This advice applies to everybody, but for people with gene variants that impair efficient folate activity in the body, it is even more important to maintain a diet that is particularly folate-rich.

Many foods are excellent sources of folate (see text box "B vitamins," p. 34), and folate is also available as a dietary supplement. The recommended daily requirement of folate for adults is 400 micrograms per day, but this amount refers only to people who have normal folate metabolism. Individuals with gene-based problems with their folate activity are likely to benefit from higher amounts of folate, though the precise levels are not yet known. Given the current state of research in this area, taking a daily multivitamin containing 400 micrograms of folate in addition to eating a folate-rich diet is recommended.

SALT

Until more research-based information is available, general dietary guidelines call for eating no more than 2,300 mg (approximately 1 teaspoon) of salt per day. There is strong evidence that limiting salt intake is a simple way to prevent or reduce high blood pressure in many people. However, if you know from your gene variants that you are "salt-sensitive," limiting your salt should be a particularly high priority.

Genetic testing for heart health

Scientific studies have already linked a number of genes involved in heart health with various aspects of diet and lifestyle. This table (see "Gene testing for heart health," p. 47) lists genes that at present are commonly included in genetic screening. Numerous additional genes are being studied and are expected to be incorporated into future genetic tests.

ANTI-INFLAMMATORY FOOD FIGHT

▶ **Omega-3 fatty acids**

✓ Some oily fish – including herring, mackerel, salmon, sardines and trout – are a rich source of beneficial omega-3 fatty acids. Other fish – including tuna, catfish, cod, flounder and halibut – also contain these fatty acids but in smaller amounts.

✓ Fish oil supplements or foods fortified with omega-3 fatty acids are a convenient alternative to fish. Many lack the typical "fishy" taste or smell, which is a great advantage for people (especially kids!) who may not like fish.

✓ Among shellfish, oysters have the highest levels of omega-3 fatty acids, while crab, scallops and shrimp provide moderate amounts.

✓ Additional sources of omega-3 fatty acids are canola oil, flaxseed and flaxseed oil (see text box "Flax facts" and a variety of flax recipes p. 173), pumpkin seeds, walnuts and walnut oil and plant foods not yet widely used in the US: perilla oil and purslane.

✓ Soybean oil, which is a mix of omega-6s and omega-3s, can help boost your omega-3 intake to some extent.

✓ Foods enriched with omega-3s include certain eggs, beverages, and breads.

▶ **Other anti-inflammatory foods**

In addition to omega-3s, a number of other food ingredients can potentially reduce overall inflammation, which can be beneficial for heart health. In particular, certain plant substances called phytonutrients ("phyto" for plant) have both anti-inflammatory and antioxidant properties. For example, in studies with animals and short-term studies with humans, foods with a high content of polyphenols, an important class of phytonutrients, helped to decrease inflammation. While research is still being conducted to identify the levels of phytonutrient intake necessary to activate health benefits, in the meantime, eating the following foods in generous quantities will help your body put up a good fight against inflammation.

••• *continued* •••

ANTI-INFLAMMATORY FOOD FIGHT *(continued)*

✓ **Cocoa/dark chocolate** – Cocoa powder and dark chocolate are rich in flavonoids, a special category of polyphenols.

✓ **Purple grape products** – Purple grapes, purple grape juice and red wine are all sources of valuable polyphenols.

✓ **Tea** – Black tea or green tea, either hot or cold, are excellent sources of polyphenols.

✓ **Fruits and vegetables** – The deeply colored red, orange, yellow and blue/purple fruits and vegetables are the particularly useful ones from an antioxidant and anti-inflammatory standpoint. Grouping by color is an easy way to think about eating the variety of fruits and vegetables that promote health.

A "color me healthy" guide to fruits and vegetables	
Blue/purple	Blue or purple berries, such as bilberries, blackberries, blueberries, cranberries, elderberries; black currants, purple or black grapes, purple grape juice, plums, raisins.
Green	Broccoli, Brussels sprouts, greens (collard, mustard, turnip), kale, kiwis, parsley, spinach.
Red	Apples (with skin), capsicum peppers, cherries, raspberries, red cabbage, red currants, rhubarb, strawberries, fresh tomato and cooked tomato products.
White	Cabbage, cauliflower, dried beans and peas, garlic, grapefruit, grapefruit juice, onions (green onions, leeks, yellow onions), soybeans and soy products, turnips.
Yellow/orange	Apricots, carrots, lemons, lemon juice, oranges, orange juice, peaches, pumpkins, sweet potatoes, yellow onions, winter squash.

GENE TESTING FOR HEART HEALTH			
Area of gene's action	**Gene name**	**Gene variant**	**Major areas of diet and lifestyle that interact with gene variants**
Cholesterol regulation	Apolipoprotein E (APOE)	2, 3, 4	• Saturated fat • Cholesterol • Smoking • Alcohol • Soluble fiber • Hormone replacement therapy • Exercise
	Cholesteryl ester transfer protein (CETP)	279G>A TaqB Rsa1 D422G	
	Lipoprotein lipase (LPL)	1595C>G	
	Hepatic lipase (LIPC or HL)	-514C>T	
	E-selectin (SELE)	98G>T S128R	
Blood pressure	Guanine nucleotide-binding protein beta-3 (GNB3)	825C>T	• Blood pressure
	Angiotensin II receptor (AGTR1)	1166A>C	• Salt intake • Body weight • Exercise
	Angiotensinogen (AGT)	-6G>A M235T	
Blood clotting	Coagulation factor V (Factor 5, Leiden)	1691G>A R506Q	• Tobacco smoke • Hormone replacement therapy and oral contraceptive pill • Long distance travel • Pregnancy
	Coagulation factor II (Factor 2, prothrombin)	20210G>A	
Blood clotting and flow	Endothelial nitric oxide synthase (ENOS)	894G>T	

••• *continued* •••

GENE TESTING FOR HEART HEALTH *(continued)*			
Area of gene's action	**Gene name**	**Gene variant**	**Major areas of diet and lifestyle that interact with gene variants**
B vitamin and homocysteine metabolism	Methylenetetrahydrofolate reductase (MTHFR)	677C>T 1298A>C	• B vitamin intake, especially folate, vitamins B6 and B12 • Alcohol
	Methionine synthase (MTR)	2576A>G	
	Methionine synthase reductase (MTRR)	66A>G	
	Cystathionine beta-synthase (CβS)	699C>T	
Inflammation	Interleukin-1 beta (IL1-beta)	-511 C>T	• Foods high in omega-3 fatty acids, eg., oily fish such as salmon, flaxseeds and flaxseed oil, walnuts and walnut oil, canola • Body weight • Exercise
	Interleukin-6 (IL6)	-174G>C -634G>C	
	Tumor necrosis factor alpha (TNF-alpha)	-308G>A	
Protection against oxidative stress	Superoxide dismutase, extracellular (SOD3)	-28C>T	• Foods rich in antioxidants (high ORAC values) • Tobacco smoke and environmental toxins
	Superoxide dismutase 2 (SOD2)	760C>G	
	Cytochrome b-245a (NADH/NADPH oxidase) (CYB*A8)	H72Y	

Chapter 4

Reducing Cancer Risk

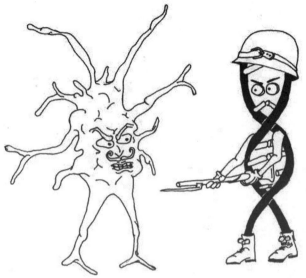

The longest-living person on record was a woman named Jeanne-Louise Calment, born in 1875 in Arles, France. Madame Calment, who remembered meeting Vincent Van Gogh in her father's shop, died in 1997 at the astonishing age of 122. Calment's longevity is remarkable enough in itself, but what's no less remarkable from a genetic point of view is that she gave up smoking only at age 117 and continued to have the occasional puff after her 118th birthday.

Granted, Madame Calment is an exception that proves the rule: smoking kills millions of people every year and irreparably damages the health of millions more. Yet how is it that some smokers suffer from years of illness and die in agony, while others, like Madame Calment, pass away peacefully at a ripe old age?

The answer lies at least in part in our genes. Madame Calment's genetic make-up must have programmed her for health and longevity, as her father lived to 94 and her mother to 86 (and these, remember, were people born in the mid-19th century, when life expectancy was significantly lower than it is today).

One of the most harrowing consequences of smoking is cancer, but people differ in their genetic susceptibility to this disease. Because of the varied genetic backgrounds of those who take up this dangerous habit, the same smokes affect different folks – with varying degrees of severity.

By changing certain behaviors while taking their genetic profiles into account, people can greatly lower their cancer risk. This chapter focuses on the body's genetic defenses against cancer that can be modified by diet and lifestyle.

Genes and cancer

Under a microscope, healthy tissue looks like a satellite photo of a neatly planned city. Cancerous tissue appears more like an unruly abstract painting, full of distorted cells bulging in all directions. This chaotic picture stems from miscommunication; while in normal body tissues the genetic "gatekeepers" that tell cells when to start dividing and when to stop are meticulously orchestrated, in cancerous tissue these controls have gone haywire. The cancerous cell contains alterations – "spelling mistakes" in the genetic code – that can have disastrous consequences. For example, if a gene that normally commands the cell to stop dividing contains an alteration, the "stop" message may arrive in garbled form (the equivalent, say, of "slop" instead of "stop"). The cell won't get the message and will continue to divide uncontrollably, encroaching on neighboring tissues.

It takes quite a few "spelling mistakes" for normal tissue to turn cancerous. In fact, research suggests that up to 10 alterations must accumulate in a single cell before it embarks on a course of uncontrolled growth. That's why cancer is a disease primarily of older persons – it can take years for so many changes to accumulate within a cell's genetic material, and most people die of other causes before cancer gets a chance to unfold. Ironically, the disease has become more common due to the success of medical science in the 20th and 21st centuries – as our lives become longer, we are giving cancer more time to develop.

But why do changes in the genetic code occur in the first place? Sometimes, they can be by-products of the cell's normal functioning – copying errors that appear when a cell duplicates its genes before dividing into 2 identical "daughter" cells. Genetic defects can also occur when the cell is assaulted by viruses, harmful chemicals, radiation or toxins present in food or tobacco smoke. Internal aggressors called free radicals can also cause genetic damage.

Parents can pass on an altered form of a gene to offspring. Such hereditary mishaps explain why cancer sometimes runs in families: several family members may have inherited the genes that predispose them to cancer. It also explains why some cancers occur early in life. The presence of inherited alterations – abnormal changes in the genetic code – gives some cancer victims a "head start" on developing the disease.

How much is due to "bad genes"?

Some inherited gene alterations strongly predispose you to developing cancer. In such cases, environmental influences play a relatively minor role. However, such cancer-triggering alterations account for a very small number of actual cancer cases. For example, 9 out of 10 women unlucky enough to inherit alterations in 2 genes – called BRCA1 and BRCA2 – have an exceptionally high chance of developing breast or ovarian cancer by age 70. However, of all women with breast cancer, only about 5 percent match this genetic profile. For the other 95 percent, the cause of cancer is much less clear.

In fact, the vast majority of cancers are triggered by factors related to the way we choose to live our lives. According to a study published in the journal *Science*, only about 5 percent of cancers are thought to be explained by genes alone, while 95 percent are believed to be due to an interaction between genes and environment, diet and lifestyle variables.

Take breast cancer, for example. Breast cancer rates in the United States are 4 to 7 times higher than in China or Japan, but when Asian women move to the US, their breast cancer risk rises over several generations until it approaches that of Caucasian American women. These women have not undergone a "gene transplant" – rather, it's the interaction of their genes with a Western lifestyle that alters their cancer risk.

This is not to suggest that, to avoid cancer, Western women should all pick up and move to Tibet. In fact, the first line of defense against cancer-causing genetic alterations is much closer to home – in every one of our body cells. Our cells are equipped with mechanisms that are remarkably effective in protecting our genes from alteration. If these mechanisms were not in place, cancer would be rampant, and life on earth would be impossible because the unified genetic code that makes us human would eventually become unrecognizable.

Part of the cell's defense strategy is based on a gene-repair "tool kit" – once a gene has been damaged, these tools swing into action to get things back to normal. (If the repair fails, the defective cell is often commanded to self-destruct.) Other defenses are aimed at removing or neutralizing potential DNA aggressors before they get a chance to cause damage. Of these, 2 types of protective mechanisms can be greatly influenced by diet – the ones that remove toxins and the ones that reduce oxidative stress.

Detoxification

The word "detox" for most of us brings up images of dysfunctional movie stars trying to kick their drug habit. But while there's no celebrity connection, cellular detoxification does come with a kick – the kick that is needed to remove potentially harmful substances from your body. Whether the unwanted material enters the body through air pollution, tobacco smoke or food, detoxification is an elaborate natural defense system aimed at minimizing the damage that can lead to disease conditions, including cancer.

Due to differences in their detoxification genes, people differ in the way they deal with toxins. Some remove them from their bodies quickly and effectively, while others may allow them to linger in the body for a dangerously long time. Poor detoxification may be a risk factor for the development of cancer; it could be one of the reasons, for example, that some people are particularly susceptible to the harmful effects of smoking. On the other hand, a robust detoxification system can be protective against potentially harmful compounds. Here's how it works:

STEP 1: PREPARING TO REMOVE THE TOXINS

Detoxification is a complex process involving many genes, but it can be separated into 2 distinct steps, called phase I and phase II. The ultimate goal of this elaborate process is to convert a potentially harmful molecule into a less dangerous one that can more readily be removed from the body (see Figure 4-1).

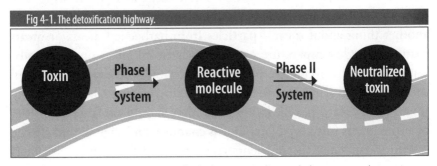

Fig 4-1. The detoxification highway.

Detoxification is a 2-step process in which the toxin is dismantled to create a less toxic, more water-soluble molecule that can be excreted from the body. In phase I, the toxin is activated, becoming a highly reactive molecule (called a "free radical"). In phase II, this molecule is chemically modified to yield a more soluble, excretable toxin.

The genes involved in the first phase activate the undesirable substance so it can be passed along the "detoxification chain" and be removed. Unfortunately, in some individuals, gene-based variations cause this activation to be either too slow or too fast.

When phase I detoxification genes are not sufficiently active, toxins build up in the body. Such reduced activity can also cause strong reactions to certain medications. This is because most medications are designed to be broken down by the body's natural detox mechanism.

If you are one of those people who can't fall asleep at night after drinking one cup of coffee in the morning, it's quite possible that your phase I genes are at least partly responsible. Caffeine is processed by phase I metabolic reactions, so people with sluggish phase I genes would do well to minimize their caffeine intake (see text box "Sources of caffeine," p. 96).

In some people, though, phase I detoxification genes work too fast, which is also not a desirable situation. Increased activity of these genes creates an abundance of activated toxins that later metabolic processes – the phase II detox mentioned above – are unable to handle efficiently.

People with overly active phase I genes should avoid smoking and refrain from eating foods that contain potentially cancer-promoting substances. Among such foods are smoked meat and smoked fish. And another thing about meat – particles from barbecued meats or meats roasted at high temperature can have a harmful effect on everybody, but people with overactive phase I genes should be especially careful to avoid overloading themselves with toxins (see text box "Avoiding toxins from meat," p. 62). In addition, they should eat large quantities of antioxidants (discussed later in this chapter), and they should also be careful to consume the nutrients recommended for people with inefficient phase II genes (see Step 2 below).

Even when your phase I system is working perfectly, it needs support from your diet. Proper activation of the toxin depends on B vitamins, as well as plant substances called polyphenols and other dietary components. A diet that includes plenty of lean protein, whole grains and foods rich in polyphenols – red, blue and purple fruits (blackberries, blueberries, cranberries, pomegranates) and their juices, as well as green tea and black tea, onions, soybean products, red wine and purple grape juice – will help this first, vital phase of detoxification to proceed smoothly.

STEP 2: EXCRETING TOXINS FROM THE BODY

Phase I detox positions a harmful molecule on the 50-yard line; phase II kicks it through the goalposts and off the playing field. The genes involved in phase II detoxification "tag" activated toxins with a small molecule that renders them water-soluble so they can be easily eliminated in urine, sweat and feces. In many people, some of these genes – referred to as glutathione S-transferases, or GSTs for short – are slightly altered or missing altogether. This prevents phase II detoxification from proceeding smoothly.

Fortunately, problematic phase II detoxification can be greatly enhanced through smart dietary choices. In particular, 2 types of vegetables are known to improve phase II detoxification: cruciferous vegetables (the cabbage and broccoli family) and allium vegetables (the onion and garlic family).

Cruciferous vegetables, named for their cross-shaped flowers, contain substances called glucosinolates that, according to the latest medical research, may offer protection against cancer and heart disease. In the body, glucosinolates are involved in processes that boost the body's detoxification mechanisms and render cancer-promoting chemicals less toxic. One study by California researchers showed that, for people missing one of the GST genes, eating broccoli approximately 4 times per week was particularly protective against colon and rectal cancers.

The other vegetables that can provide protection against cancer are the allium vegetables, such as onions, garlic, shallots and leeks. Thanks to a number of compounds that account both for their distinctive smell and for many of their beneficial properties, these vegetables work hand-in-hand with the body's detoxification system, making it more efficient. In addition, allium vegetables contain antioxidants, which promote health by neutralizing free radicals and minimizing their damage to the body (see Reducing oxidative stress, below).

While all allium vegetables are good for you, much research has focused specifically on garlic. When crushed, garlic produces a substance called allicin, which protects the garlic plant from insects and other invaders. Along with its talent as a bug repellant, allicin appears to reduce the risk of cancer as well as thrombosis (blood clot formation) – another health-harming condition.

To sum up: eating a diet rich in cruciferous and allium vegetables is healthy for everyone. However, if your genes are not terribly good at ridding your body of toxins, developing a taste for broccoli and garlic may reduce your risk of cancer and is definitely the way to go (see text box "Cruciferous and allium vegetables – detox champs!," p. 57).

Reducing oxidative stress

Anyone who has seen apple slices turn brown when left out in the air has encountered oxidation. The process is a biochemical reaction in which molecules in the apple interact with oxygen to produce a brown pigment– a kind of "molecular rust." Similarly, molecules in our bodies can undergo oxidation. While our bodies have an elaborate system for protecting us against the ravages of oxidation and "living in oxygen" has obvious, life-preserving advantages, sometimes the level of damage exceeds what our bodies can handle.

The oxidation process generates highly reactive, unstable molecules – essentially, loose cannonballs that, if left unchecked, career around in our

CRUCIFEROUS AND ALLIUM VEGETABLES – DETOX CHAMPS!

▸ A major subgroup of cruciferous vegetables is the Brassica family, which includes Brussels sprouts, broccoli, cabbage, cauliflower, kale, kohlrabi, turnips and watercress.

▸ Avoid overcooking cruciferous vegetables. Lightly steam them so they retain their color, structure and nutrient content. You can also eat them raw, perhaps with a dip or as part of a snack or lunch.

▸ Allium vegetables include chives, garlic, leeks, onions, spring onions, green onions and shallots.

▸ Garlic can be taken as a supplement, but it is not considered to be as effective as eating fresh or lightly cooked garlic.

bodies and damage DNA, proteins and the membranes that surround each cell. These loose cannonballs, called free radicals, have an unpaired electron that steals an electron from a neighboring molecule to make a pair. This electron balancing act, however, causes the robbed molecules to become reactive, and so on, resulting in a domino effect scientists refer to as oxidative stress.

Oxidative stress disrupts the order and functioning of cells and is believed to be involved in cancer, as well as in aging, heart disease, chronic inflammation and other conditions. Environmental pollution and smoking increase the production of free radicals. Other culprits include the consumption of certain foods, including oils that have deteriorated from standing at room temperature or from being exposed to light (this is the reason experts recommend storing oils in the refrigerator in dark-colored glass bottles).

Fortunately, there is a way to break the oxidative stress cycle and lower the risk of disease. Certain foods contain unique molecules – called antioxidants – that balance free radicals without themselves becoming unbalanced. Antioxidants interrupt the domino effect of oxidative stress and prevent free radicals from pursuing their health-damaging activities.

Another defense against oxidative stress is coded right into our genes. Body cells have their own system, including a much-studied enzyme produced by the MnSOD gene (pronounced "Em-S-O-D", short for manganese superoxide dismutase). This enzyme scavenges free radicals, preventing them from reacting uncontrollably with various parts of the cell and thus causing damage and disease.

The antioxidant activity described above is strongly affected by diet. For example, a 1999 study reported in the journal *Cancer Research* found that in premenopausal women, the risk of breast cancer increased with certain variants of the MnSOD gene. However, this risk was most pronounced among women who consumed insufficient amounts of fruit and vegetables, which serve as rich sources for a variety of antioxidants.

So what does this all mean for you? To ensure that your body does not suffer from the ill effects of oxidative stress, it's important that you give it the antioxidants it needs. True even if your antioxidant genes are completely normal, this advice becomes crucial if you carry variants of MnSOD – or other genes – that slow down antioxidant activity. By increasing your dietary intake of antioxidants – through fruits and vegetables and a wide variety of other foods (see text box "Antioxidant-rich foods," p. 63) – you can help your body defend itself against cancer.

Reducing your risk of cancer the gene-smart way

Contrary to popular belief, cancer is largely preventable. Experts believe that at least half of all cancer deaths could be avoided by eliminating smoking and other risky behaviors and by adopting other sound lifestyle practices. Below is a list of recommendations that will help you reduce your risk, with a special emphasis on anti-cancer advice that can be tailored to your DNA.

ARE YOU AT RISK FOR CANCER?

▶ **Family history**
Do you have several relatives, particularly parents or siblings, who developed cancer? At what age did your relatives develop the cancer? (This is a crucial consideration in assessing your cancer risk; if your mother were diagnosed with a cancerous tumor at age 70, her cancer could have resulted from damage that accumulated during her life and not necessarily from inherited genetic defects that she could have passed on to you.)

▶ **Genetic screening**
Did genetic screening reveal that you have gene variants associated with increased cancer risk?

▶ **Tobacco use**
Do you smoke?

▶ **Exposure to toxic chemicals**
Are you exposed to cancer-promoting chemicals in your home or workplace?

▶ **Diet**
Are you eating a diet that minimizes cancer risk – particularly, a diet rich in fruits and vegetables?

The questions above are intended only as a general guide. To assess your risk of cancer you will need to consult your health care practitioner, particularly if you suspect that you may have inherited a predisposition to the disease.

FRUITS AND VEGETABLES

The current recommendation is to eat a minimum of 5 and, preferably, 9 to 10, servings of a combination of fruits and vegetables a day (see text box "What's a serving?" for common serving sizes, p. 64).

Dietary supplements of concentrated fruit and vegetables are increasingly popular and may be helpful to supplement the number you eat each day.

However, you should choose whole fruits and vegetables whenever possible to take advantage of their fiber, water and many additional beneficial substances that we're only beginning to identify. And of course, fruits and vegetables are a great – and low-calorie – way to relieve hunger.

WHOLE GRAINS
Choose whole grains rather than processed (refined) grains.

REFINED SUGAR
Keep your sugar intake to a minimum. Simple sugars such as table sugar and other highly refined sugars appear to be a favorite source of fuel for cancer cells. (See text box "What's in a name? Finding the hidden sugar" on p. 61 for terms that signal the presence of sugar in a food product.)

MEAT
Limit fatty or processed meats (see text box "Avoiding toxins from meat," p. 62).

EXERCISE
There are plenty of reasons to be physically active, and reducing cancer risk is one of them. For example, a recent review of medical literature suggests that the risk of colon cancer in physically active men and women is 30 to 40 percent lower compared with inactive persons, and that the risk of breast cancer in physically active women is reduced by approximately 20 to 30 percent. It appears that 30 to 60 minutes of moderate to vigorous physical activity a day is needed to decrease the risk (see text boxes "Exercise advice" p. 132 and "Tips to keep you exercising," p. 135).

WEIGHT
Maintain a healthy weight throughout your lifetime.

ALCOHOL
If you drink alcohol, do so in moderation (see text box "What is moderate drinking?" p. 37).

WHAT'S IN A NAME? FINDING THE HIDDEN SUGAR

A food is likely to be high in sugar if one of these terms appears first or second in the ingredient list, or if a number of these terms appear in the list:

- Brown sugar
- Caramel
- Confectioners' sugar (powdered sugar)
- Corn sweetener
- Corn syrup
- Date sugar
- Dextrin
- Dextrose
- Fructose
- Fruit juice concentrate
- Fruit sugar
- Glucose
- High-fructose corn syrup
- Honey
- Invert sugar

- Lactose
- Levulose
- Maltose
- Malt syrup
- Mannitol
- Maple syrup
- Molasses
- Polydextrose
- Raw sugar
- Sorbitol
- Sucrose
- Sugar
- Syrup
- Table sugar
- Turbinado sugar

Major sources of sugar in today's food choices include:
- Soft drinks
- Cakes, cookies and pies
- Candy
- Dairy desserts, such as ice cream and sherbet
- Fruitades and drinks such as fruit punch and lemonade

SMOKING

Quitting smoking is a good idea for everyone today – even the best defense system is greatly challenged by the toxins that enter your body with every puff. But if you have gene variants that impair your detoxification and antioxidant mechanisms, it is absolutely imperative that you quit smoking and avoid second-hand smoke.

AVOIDING TOXINS FROM MEAT

A high level of toxins has been implicated in a number of disease conditions, including cancer. Here are some tips for keeping meat-derived toxins at a minimum.

▶ Cooking temperature is the most important factor in the formation of toxic substances in meat. Frying, chargrilling, broiling and barbecuing produce the largest amounts of toxins because these cooking methods use high temperatures that affect the fat.

▶ Grilling generates a charred residue that is thought to be potentially harmful. The fat dripping on hot coals or a hot roasting pan generates toxic substances called polyaromatic hydrocarbons (PAHs), which have been implicated in cancer development. Meats that are partially cooked in the microwave and then finished by other cooking methods have lower levels of PAHs. Time is also a factor: meat cooked for a long time by any method will form more toxins.

▶ You don't need to banish meat from your diet, however. Use lean cuts of meat and poultry, reduce the frequency of meat-based meals and pay particular attention to how you cook it. Pre-cook meats in the oven or microwave, then briefly grill for flavor. Marinating meat before grilling is believed to drastically reduce the amount of toxins formed on the grill.

▶ Keep meat portions small so they need less time on the grill, and remove all charred or burned portions before serving.

▶ Smoked foods may taste terrific – but they make use of chemicals that can combine with natural substances in meat and fish to form potentially toxic compounds. Avoid eating smoked meat and fish whenever possible, but if you do occasionally enjoy these foods, balance your meal with vitamin C-rich choices, such as lemon juice or tomatoes, which help neutralize the effects of the toxins.

▶ Similarly, the nitrites used to treat meats, such as bologna, ham and bacon, and that produce their characteristic pink color, is also thought to increase the risk of developing cancer. Eliminate or at least greatly limit the amount of nitrite-treated foods you select.

▶ Include soy products, such as soybeans, soy cheese, tofu and soymilk in your meals. They are excellent sources of protein and appear to be beneficial in preventing cancer.

▶ When choosing a protein source, use dried beans and peas as an alternative to meat. Chickpeas, a wide range of lentils, split peas, butter beans, blackeyed peas, kidney beans, navy beans and pinto beans are all excellent sources of protein.

▶ Finally a word about balancing meat meals: to help keep meat intake down to a desirable level, picture your plate. Two-thirds of it should be filled with plant foods such as vegetables, fruits, whole grains and dried beans and peas. Only one-third should be filled with animal products.

Antioxidant-rich foods

Antioxidants protect our cells against oxidative stress, a harmful condition caused by destructive molecules called free radicals. To evaluate the antioxidant power of foods and other substances, scientists at Tufts University in Boston have developed a laboratory test that measures what's known as Oxygen Radical Absorbance Capacity, or ORAC. The higher the ORAC value, the greater the food's potency as an antioxidant. The table below lists fruits and vegetables that rank highest in terms of their ORAC score. Note that the darker-colored fruits and vegetables typically have the highest ORAC values.

ANTIOXIDANT-RICH FOODS			
Fruits	**ORAC value**	**Vegetables**	**ORAC value**
Prunes	5,770	Kale	1,770
Raisins	2,830	Spinach, raw	1,260
Blueberries	2,400	Brussels sprouts	980
Blackberries	2,036	Alfalfa sprouts	930
Cranberries	1,750	Spinach, steamed	909
Strawberries	1,540	Broccoli florets	890
Raspberries	1.220	Beets	841
Plums	949	Red bell pepper	713
Oranges	750	Onion	450
Grapes, red	739	Corn	400
Cherries	670	Eggplant	390

Source: USDA Human Nutrition Research Center on Aging at Tufts University, published in Agricultural Research, February 1999.

What's a serving?

The size of a recommended serving is generally smaller than we might think. This is good news when it comes to eating at least 5 servings of fruits and vegetables a day but bad news when we realize just how small a muffin or scoop of ice cream should be!

WHAT'S A SERVING?

▶ **Fruits**

One serving of fruit can be:

½ cup of cut fruit – fresh, canned or frozen (any fruit counts)

6 ounces of any 100 percent fruit juice (¾ cup)

¼ cup of dried fruit

1 medium whole fruit

½ medium grapefruit

1 small or ½ large banana

15 seedless grapes

¾ cup berries

▶ **Vegetables**

One serving of vegetables – whole, cut-up or mashed – can be:

1 cup of fresh, frozen, canned, cooked or dried/dehydrated vegetables (any vegetable counts)

6 ounces of any 100 percent vegetable juice (¾ cup)

1 cup of raw leafy greens

2 broccoli spears 5" long, raw or cooked

1 small sweet potato

1 large carrot or 8 baby carrots

1 large raw whole tomato

Helpful visual tricks for "eye-balling" an appropriate serving size:

	Serving Size	Visual equivalent
Fruits	1 medium fruit	Baseball
	½ cup cut fruit	Baseball
	¼ cup dried fruit	Large egg
	¾ cup berries	Baseball
Vegetables	1 cup salad greens	Baseball
	½ cup cooked vegetable	Fist
	1 baked potato	Fist

Genetic testing for cancer risk

Scientific studies have already shown a link between diet and lifestyle and a number of genes involved in the risk of cancer. The table below lists genes that are commonly included in genetic screening. Numerous additional genes are being studied and are expected to be incorporated into future genetic tests.

GENE TESTING FOR CANCER RISK			
Area of gene's action	Gene name	Gene variant	Major areas of diet and lifestyle that interact with gene variants
Phase I Detoxification	CYP1A1	3801T>C (m1, Msp1) 2455A>G (m2)	• Food carcinogens such as heterocyclic amines (HCAs), polycyclic aromatic hydrocarbons (PAH) and nitrosamines
	CYP2C19	Multiple	• Cruciferous vegetables, eg., broccoli and cauliflower
	CYP3A4	Multiple	• Allium vegetables, eg., onions and garlic • Tobacco smoke
	CYP2C9	Multiple	• Warfarin • Sulphonylureas
	CYP2D6	Multiple	• The metabolism of 20% of all prescription drugs is affected by this gene • Tobacco smoke
	CYP2E1	*5 (Rsal)	• Alcohol • Nitrosamines
••• *continued* •••			

65

GENE TESTING FOR CANCER RISK *(continued)*			
Area of gene's action	Gene name	Gene variant	Major areas of diet and lifestyle that interact with gene variants
Phase II Detoxification	N-acetyltransferase 1 (NAT1)	R64W R187Q	• Food carcinogens such as heterocyclic amines (HCAs), polycyclic aromatic hydrocarbons (PAHs) and nitrosamines • Cruciferous vegetables, eg., broccoli and cauliflower • Allium vegetables, eg., onions and garlic • Tobacco smoke
	N-acetyltransferase 2 (NAT2)	I114T R197Q G286E R64Q K268R	
	Glutathione S-transferase M1 (GSTM1)	INS/DEL	
	Glutathione S-transferase T1 (GSTT1)	INS/DEL	
	Glutathione S-transferase P1 (GSTP1)	313A>G 341C>T	
Protection against oxidative stress	Superoxide dismutase 1 (SOD1)	G93A A4V	• Foods rich in antioxidants (high ORAC values) • Tobacco smoke and environmental toxins
	Superoxide dismutase 2 (SOD2)	-28C>T (Ala16Val)	
	Superoxide dismutase, extracellular (SOD3)	760C>G	
Estrogen exposure	Catecholamine-O-methyl transferase (COMT)	472G>A	• B vitamin intake, especially folate, vitamins B6 and B12 • Phytoestrogen intake (converts estrogens and other chemicals to non-toxic compounds)
DNA repair and synthesis	Methylenetetrahy-drofolate reductase (MTHFR)	677C>T 1298A>C	• B vitamin intake, especially folate, vitamins B6 and B12

Chapter 5

Preventing Diabetes

Southern Arizona's sizzling Sonoran Desert is the setting for a dramatic example of the interdependence between genes and lifestyle. The Pima Indians who live in the Sonaran have a dubious distinction – an unusually high proportion of them are obese and a full 54 percent of the men have diabetes, one of the highest rates of this disease in the world. Genetically speaking, the Sonoran Pimas are closely related to the Pima Indians living just across the border, in Northern Mexico's Sierra Madre mountain range. However, in contrast to their American counterparts, those Pima Indians who live in Mexico are generally lean and have low rates of diabetes.

This curious disparity is attributed to lifestyle: the Pimas of Arizona tend to be sedentary and consume 50 percent of their calories as fat, as well as large amounts of refined carbohydrates. The Indians in Mexico eat a traditional Pima diet in which carbohydrates are less refined, and only about 20 percent of their energy comes from fat. Moreover, they are physically active as farmers, sawmill workers and builders. Thus, whatever genetic predisposition the Pimas may have toward diabetes comes to the fore only in the presence of harmful lifestyle triggers – in the form of a sedentary lifestyle and an unhealthy diet.

The Sonoran Desert story is far from a provincial concern. In fact, what happened to the Pima Indians in the United States is now occurring on a much larger scale to the population worldwide. In all Westernized parts of the planet, people are consuming an unprecedented amount of fat and sugar while eating less whole grains, fiber, fruits and vegetables and getting less physical exercise. In today's fatter, less fit world, rates of diabetes are soaring.

Epidemiologists – those researchers who study the cause and spread of disease – are sounding the alarm, terming the recent rise in diabetes an epidemic. From 1980 to 2005, the number of Americans with diabetes more than doubled, and the disease is now believed to affect more than 20 million. The disease is also on the increase in developing countries, particularly in urbanized areas. Worldwide, the number of people with diabetes is estimated to be around 200 million and, if current trends continue, it might become one of the most common diseases in the world, affecting about 330 million people by 2025.

Just like an infectious disease, the diabetes epidemic involves an environmental risk factor – specifically, a harmful lifestyle. But along with the damaging effects of Western living on our waistlines, there is also a genetic factor. According to the late James Neel, MD, PhD, a renowned professor of human genetics at the University of Michigan, the diabetes epidemic can be explained at least in part by the "thrifty gene" theory.

Dr. Neel argued that, for thousands of years, people who made a living by farming, hunting and fishing went through alternating periods of feast and famine. While dealing with this life-threatening variability in calorie supply, those who had a few "thrifty genes" – genes that allowed them to build up fat during times of plenty so as to avoid starvation during famine – had a survival advantage.

With the shift to a Western lifestyle, food has become abundant year round, and it no longer requires heroic acts of physical exertion to fill up our plates. However, our "thrifty genes" don't know this, and continue to help us stash away calories – and lots of them – in the form of fat. Thus, according to Dr. Neel's theory, the same genes that saved our ancient ancestors from starvation now expose modern humans to the health risks of being overweight. And one of the most worrisome consequences of being overweight is the greatly increased risk of developing diabetes.

What is diabetes?

To provide us with the energy we need to go about our daily activities, our body cells rely on the sugar known as glucose. Much of what we think of as "digesting our food" involves converting what we eat into glucose in order to provide the body with a ready supply of energy. While some glucose is used by body cells on an ongoing basis, some of it is also stored for future use – in the liver, in muscle tissues or in the form of fat.

Glucose is delivered to body cells with the help of insulin – a hormone produced in the pancreas. When the body does not make enough insulin, or when the cells do not respond properly to the insulin that's present, sugar levels rise to abnormally high levels. This, in a nutshell, is diabetes (see Figure 5-1).

There are 2 major types of diabetes. Type 1 diabetes is an autoimmune disorder, in which the body mistakenly attacks the insulin-producing cells in the pancreas, decreasing the amount of secreted insulin.

Sometimes called juvenile diabetes, it occurs mainly in children and adolescents, and its onset is usually clear-cut and dramatic.

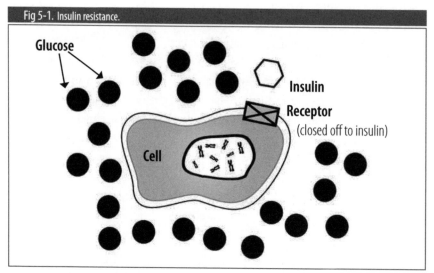

Fig 5-1. Insulin resistance.

Glucose

Insulin

Receptor
(closed off to insulin)

Cell

Insulin is unable to "dock" onto receptors on the surface of cells and allow glucose to enter. Cells are starved for energy-producing glucose, which accumulates outside the cells in the bloodstream and causes health problems.

Type 2 diabetes, the more common form, is caused by a combination of genes and lifestyle. Until recently, type 2 diabetes occurred mainly in people over 40. Now it's becoming increasingly common in children and young adults, thanks to the oversized meals and junk food habits that are causing more and more young people to put on weight. In fact, studies suggest that among overweight American teens, as many as 1 in 6 has abnormally high blood sugar levels when measured after an overnight fast (called "fasting blood sugar") – a sign of an increased risk of diabetes.

In contrast to type 1 diabetes, type 2 generally unfolds gradually. Many people first develop resistance to insulin, which disrupts proper glucose metabolism. Even when they go on to develop full-blown diabetes, at first there may be no symptoms at all, and it often takes several years for the condition to be detected. During this period, however, diabetes-triggered distortions in body metabolism are silently taking their toll.

Eventually, elevated sugar levels in the blood lead to excessive urination and a constant feeling of thirst and hunger. And this is only the beginning; in time, diabetes can lead to kidney disease, impaired eyesight or even blindness, and ulcers on the feet that in severe cases can lead to amputation. People with type 2 diabetes also have a significantly increased risk for heart disease.

The genetics of type 2 diabetes

There is no question that the alarming increase in diabetes cases over the past decade can be traced to changes induced by the widespread adoption of a Western lifestyle. However, these changes seem to trigger the disease only in people who already carry a genetic predisposition for diabetes. Fortunately for people who have a gene-based susceptibility to developing type 2 diabetes, the appropriate lifestyle choices can keep the disease at bay.

Type 2 diabetes runs in families. Some studies indicate that if you have a parent with diabetes, you have a 40 percent chance of eventually developing the disease yourself. However, parents and their children share more than just genes; with family members often sharing similar environments, cultures and habits, it can be difficult to identify a single, decisive factor leading to diabetes onset.

As with other complex diseases – conditions in which both genetic and environmental factors play a role – the relative contribution of genes to the development of type 2 diabetes emerges most clearly from studies of twins. Identical twins – who share exactly the same genes – do not automatically share the disease. In fact, if one of a pair of identical twins has diabetes, the chances of the other twin developing the condition, while high, is still only between 50 to 90 percent.

It's Not Just Your Genes!

Twins who grow up together certainly tend to have similar lifestyles, but that's true both of identical and non-identical twins. Among identical twins, the higher correlation in diabetes rates can be accounted for by their shared genetic make-up. On the other hand, the figures clearly show that genetic predisposition is far from a final verdict, as so many people do not develop diabetes despite having the same genes as their diabetes-stricken identical twin.

Physicians have long noted that type 2 diabetes seems to "cluster" together with risk factors usually associated with heart disease. This group of factors is referred to in the medical literature as the metabolic syndrome, insulin resistance syndrome or – perhaps as a nod to the mysterious link between its various symptoms – syndrome X. Risk factors associated with the metabolic syndrome include an increased incidence of abdominal obesity (an "apple" shape) and high blood pressure, along with low levels of "good" (HDL) cholesterol and high levels of "bad" (LDL) cholesterol and triglycerides. The clustering of these risks suggests the presence of an underlying genetic vulnerability that predisposes a person to the "double whammy" of both diabetes and heart disease.

As one of its alternative names suggests, a major feature of the metabolic syndrome is insulin resistance – a decreased sensitivity to the hormone that helps metabolize blood sugar. When this condition develops, the pancreas – which may be producing sufficient insulin – begins to compensate for the body's sluggish response by stepping up production, causing levels of insulin in the blood to become abnormally high. The genes associated with insulin resistance are being intensively studied, as this condition is almost always a forerunner of full-blown, type 2 diabetes.

When unraveling the mysteries of a chronic and widespread condition like type 2 diabetes, it would be nice if scientists could pinpoint a single gene that is the cause of all the trouble – and, of course, magically "fix" it. Unfortunately, experts think there is probably no such gene. Rather, there appear to be many genes, each having a small effect. This is also true in the case of insulin resistance; some genes associated with this condition do not appear to be directly related to insulin, and instead affect other body processes, such as inflammation. Complicating matters further, all the genes associated with type 2 diabetes interact with each other as well as with the environment.

But even if we cannot currently solve the entire puzzle, correcting even a small genetic mishap can help slow the frightening progress of the worldwide diabetes epidemic.

The case of the "thrifty" gene

Remember Dr. Neel, and his "thrifty" genes? Well, one of the most important of these "coupon clippers" may be a gene called PPAR-gamma (pronounced "pee-par-gamma"). Linked to diabetes since 1997 and extensively studied ever since, PPAR-gamma appears to regulate energy storage and insulin sensitivity. Certain diabetic drugs that improve insulin sensitivity (the thiazolidenediones, or TZDs) do so by acting on this gene.

Like other genes discussed in this book, PPAR-gamma appears in different variants in different people. A certain form of this gene, referred to as Pro12Ala, seems to be protective against the development of diabetes. It is present in about 15 to 20 percent of Caucasians, but in certain ethnic groups – those groups particularly prone to diabetes – this form of the gene may be rare. For example, in one study, only 1.9 percent of African Americans had the protective variant. While the rarity of this gene variant might not fully explain the high rates of diabetes among African Americans, it does suggest a connection between diabetes and the PPAR-gamma gene.

But while examining this particular gene variant, scientists found themselves faced with a big, fat question. How does the variant of the PPAR-gamma gene protect people against type 2 diabetes? It turned out that this gene variant did not – as scientists had originally assumed – play a direct role in forestalling the formation of diabetes-promoting fat tissue. Instead, the PPAR-gamma gene emerged as a classic nutrigenomic gene: its variants produced their impact not by themselves but only in combination with certain dietary practices, in this case, the type of fat in a person's diet.

When researchers examined the types of fat their subjects were eating, they discovered that the protective variant seemed to help people keep their weight down only when their diet featured a healthy ratio of polyunsaturated to saturated fats. That is, when people ate a significantly greater amount of polyunsaturated than saturated fats, the protective variant of the PPAR-gamma gene could exert its beneficial effect on weight. However, when the ratio was poor – and intake of saturated fats exceeded the polyunsaturated ones – all bets were off, and the protection no longer worked!

Interestingly, in terms of the impact of total fat intake, there was no difference between people with the protective gene variant or without. It was the type rather than the amount of fat that mattered.

So in terms of avoiding type 2 diabetes, here's the skinny: for people with the protective form of the PPAR-gamma gene, important advice for preventing diabetes may be to monitor the kind of fats they consume. Nutritional genomics – personal, science-based diet advice – strikes again!

Triple risk

In 1996, a study of Mexican Americans in Starr County, Texas – a population group that has a diabetes rate of higher than 10 percent – revealed another player on the type 2 gene team: CAPN10 (pronounced "cap-n-10", short for calpain-10). This gene codes for the calpain-10 enzyme, believed to be involved in breaking down proteins.

By scanning the entire genome of individuals with diabetes, as well as their brothers and sisters, scientists zeroed in on a certain version of CAPN10, referred to as 112/121. This version is associated with a threefold increase in diabetes risk and appears to be more common among Mexican Americans than other ethnic groups. Although it is unclear whether the 112/121 version of CAPN10 plays a role in diabetes development in other ethnicities, in some specific population groups it may indeed have an effect. For example, in Pima Indians of Arizona, who, as mentioned earlier, have high rates of diabetes, this variant of the CAPN10 gene appears to be associated with insulin resistance.

Gene variants that increase the risk of diabetes – like the one described above – can be enormously valuable to medical science, because they can be used to identify diabetes susceptibility early in life, before the disease has a chance to develop. This mounting genetic evidence is starting to affect the way doctors do business.

For example, in 2005 researchers published a study of some 2,300 people in Finland. For 12 years, the investigators had studied people with different versions of the 2 genes discussed in this chapter – PPAR-gamma and CAPN10 – and found that the risk of diabetes was increased more than 20-fold in obese people with certain variants of these 2 genes and elevated fasting blood sugar levels. This study provides hard evidence that it is indeed possible to predict who is most likely to develop diabetes by looking at the person's genes. In the conclusion of their report, the researchers state what, from a nutrigenomic point of view, has already become obvious: "Genetic testing might become a future approach to identifying individuals at risk of type 2 diabetes."

Luckily, when it comes to type 2 diabetes, genetic predisposition and development of the disease itself are two separate things. Diabetes and its potential precursor, insulin resistance, are quite responsive to diet and exercise. This means that early genetic identification of risk can make it possible to take concrete and effective action.

ARE YOU AT RISK FOR DIABETES?

Health care professionals suspect that more than 6 million Americans — about one-third of all people with type 2 diabetes in the United States — have the disease but don't know it. Yet the earlier this condition is diagnosed, the better the chance of reducing its harmful consequences. To evaluate your risk of diabetes, consider the following:

▶ **Weight**
Are you overweight? Type 2 diabetes is far more common among the obese. In one study, the risk of diabetes was increased 20-fold in women with a body mass index of more than 30. (For an explanation on how to check your body mass index, see p. 103.)

▶ **Age**
How old are you? The risk of diabetes increases with age, particularly after 45.

▶ **Physical activity**
Do you exercise regularly? Sedentary lifestyle is a risk factor for diabetes.

▶ **Family history**
Do you have first-degree relatives — a parent, sister, brother or child — with diabetes?

▶ **Genetic screening**
Did genetic screening reveal that you have gene variants associated with increased diabetes risk?

▶ **Metabolic syndrome**
Do you show signs of the metabolic syndrome — the combination of symptoms that may include high blood pressure, abdominal obesity, high levels of "bad" (LDL) cholesterol, low levels of "good" (HDL) cholesterol, high levels of triglycerides and insulin resistance? This syndrome is a "red flag" warning of impending, full-blown diabetes.

▶ **Polycystic ovarian syndrome**
Do you have polycystic ovarian syndrome (PCOS)?

▶ **Gestational diabetes**
Did you have diabetes in pregnancy ("gestational diabetes")?

The questions above are intended only as a general guide. To assess your risk of diabetes, consult a health care professional who will determine how well your body handles the sugar you eat and conduct other appropriate tests. And remember, the good news about type 2 diabetes is that it responds exceptionally well to diet and exercise!

Preventing type 2 diabetes the gene-smart way

Even if you have reason to believe that you are genetically predisposed to type 2 diabetes, you can dramatically reduce your chances of developing this condition by taking preventive measures. This has been demonstrated by several studies, most notably the large-scale 2002 trial called the Diabetes Prevention Program, sponsored by the National Institutes of Health. Following more than 3,200 overweight Americans at risk for type 2 diabetes, the study showed that participants were able to reduce their risk by nearly 60 percent through moderate exercise of about 30 minutes a day and a weight loss of 5 to 7 percent. For this type of diabetes, lifestyle changes were shown to be twice as effective as drug therapy!

Below are suggestions for reducing your risk of diabetes.

Please note that this advice is for healthy people. If you already have diabetes, you need to consult a health care professional for personal recommendations, which will be based on the type of diabetes you have as well as on other criteria. And, as always, if you've already done a complete screening for nutrigenomic factors, you will achieve even better results as these general recommendations will be adjusted to your own genetic profile.

WEIGHT
Weight loss is recommended for all overweight people who have diabetes or are at risk of the disease. It's important to set achievable and maintainable goals. Even a moderate weight loss – about 5 percent of body weight – can improve insulin sensitivity and produce other health benefits. It can be difficult to lose weight, but knowing that weight loss

provides the surest path to reducing your diabetes risk may give you the extra motivation you need.

INSULIN RESISTANCE

Medical tests can tell you whether you are insulin-resistant. If you are, this dark cloud still has a silver lining: overweight people with insulin resistance benefit more from weight loss than overweight people having normal insulin sensitivity.

The type of testing appropriate for you will depend upon your state of health. If you have a family history of diabetes or have experienced gestational diabetes but have not developed type 2 diabetes, you may want to investigate genetic screening. If you already have symptoms of the metabolic syndrome, your health care provider can best assist you in assessing your risk of developing type 2 diabetes.

PHYSICAL ACTIVITY

Get out your sneakers – a regular program of vigorous physical activity is key to lowering your diabetes risk. Both regular aerobic exercise and strength conditioning have positive effects on insulin sensitivity and blood sugar levels, as well as on weight. Moreover, physical activity adds to your heart health, bone health and mental sharpness.

Being fit is important for everyone, but it is especially important if you have family members with type 2 diabetes. Most studies suggest that 30 to 60 minutes daily of moderately intense exercise, such as brisk walking or jogging are needed to keep you fit and to keep your weight low over the long term. Exercise does not need to occur in a single session to be beneficial; dividing your workout into short bouts spaced throughout the day will produce a similar benefit and may be easier to maintain over time (see boxes "Exercise advice" p. 132 and "Tips to keep you exercising," p. 135). Don't despair if this is way more time than you have. Shoot for these goals and remember that some exercise is usually better than none. Do what you can, and ditch the guilt!

FIBER

Include whole grains and other sources of fiber among your food choices. Dietary fiber has been found to increase satiety, help lower blood sugar levels, decrease the absorption of dietary fat and help to reduce high blood pressure.

FAT

According to the Centers for Disease Control and Prevention, about two-thirds of Americans eat more total fat – and in particular, more saturated fat – than what is recommended to lower the risk of developing diabetes. Keep your fat intake between 20 and 35 percent of total calories consumed and, when you do choose fatty foods, select omega-3s and other polyunsaturated fats rather than saturated fats.

To remind you: saturated fats are those yummy fats in butter and other whole fat dairy products, solid margarine, milk chocolate, sweet rolls and other baked goods. Delicious as these fats taste, they're major artery-cloggers and are best eaten as rare treats.

To lower your level of saturated fats, choose fats such as those found in nuts, olives and olive oil, peanuts and peanut oil, canola oil, cold-water fish and their oils, walnut oil, flaxseed and flaxseed oil. (See text box "Know your fats!" on p. 40 for food sources of different types of fat.) If you switch to the more health-promoting fats, be sure not to increase your intake of total calories, in order to prevent weight gain.

Genetic testing for the risk of insulin resistance and diabetes

Scientific studies have already established a link between diet and lifestyle and a number of genes involved in the risk of developing insulin resistance and diabetes. The table below lists genes that are commonly included in genetic screening. Numerous additional genes are being studied and are expected to be incorporated into future genetic tests.

GENE TESTING FOR THE RISK OF INSULIN RESISTANCE AND DIABETES			
Area of gene's action	**Gene name**	**Gene variant**	**Major areas of diet and lifestyle that interact with gene variants**
Insulin secretion Fat breakdown	Vitamin D receptor (VDR)	Taq1 Bsml Fok1	• Saturated fat • Carbohydrate • Body weight • Exercise
Glucose and fat metabolism	Peroxisome proliferator-activated receptor-gamma (PPAR-gamma)	Pro12Ala	• Fats • Carbohydrate • Body weight • Exercise
Blood flow/pressure Salt balance	Angiotensin converting enzyme (ACE)	INS/DEL	• Saturated fat • Carbohydrate • Body weight • Exercise
Insulin secretion Insulin sensitivity Inflammation	Interleukin-6 (IL6)	-174G>C -634G>C	• Foods high in omega-3 fatty acids, eg., oily fish such as salmon, flaxseed and flaxseed oil, walnuts and walnut oil, canola oil • Body weight • Exercise
	Tumor necrosis factor alpha (TNF-alpha)	-308G>A	

Chapter 6

Bone Health

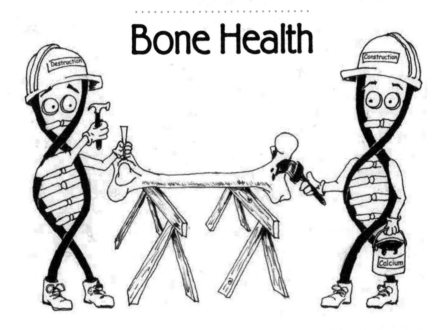

For three years in the late 1990s, 96 women in Omaha, Nebraska, drank coffee in the name of science. The women, aged 65 to 77, were at least 3-cup-a-day drinkers – in other words, they all took in a daily dose of more than 300 mg of caffeine. While the women were enjoying their brew, researchers from nearby Creighton University studied the changes that were taking place in the women's bones. All the subjects lost some bone mass during this period – a common phenomenon, especially in older women, that makes bones weaker and more likely to break. However, in some of the subjects, this change was dangerously rapid. These women didn't differ from the others in any factor known to be relevant to bone health. So why did they lose bone mass at such a strikingly accelerated pace?

Apparently, the answer lay hidden in the women's genes. Those who suffered from the rapid loss of bone mass all had a specific gene variant – one that made them particularly susceptible to the bone-weakening effects of caffeine. As a result, for them, heavy coffee drinking had an especially harmful effect.

The Nebraska coffee study demonstrates the important role genes play in determining the long-term health of your bones. However, it also illustrates how this role can play out differently, depending on your behavior. The fact is, while your genes may predispose you to the loss of bone mass in the presence of caffeine, your skeleton is still relatively safe from this effect until you take up a permanent seat at the local coffeehouse – and start indulging in several cups of java every day.

Although genes are significant, diet and exercise are known to be enormously important for keeping our skeletons strong. In this chapter, we will discuss how genes and lifestyle come together to make – or break – the health of your bones.

Bone function and structure

Just as a powerful car or aircraft cannot function without a sturdy frame, the human body cannot maintain a vital, vigorous existence without healthy bones. Our bones, however, do more than just provide us with mechanical support. They also serve as a reservoir of calcium, an essential mineral. Calcium is a central player in a wide range of cellular functions; we extract it from our bones whenever calcium levels in the blood are low. Such "calcium mining," however, comes at a price – the more calcium that is removed from our bones, the less stays behind to help keep the bones strong and rigid.

But why do our bones need help in the first place? Why doesn't our skeleton – like any other type of structural "scaffolding" – remain more or less the same throughout our lives? Hidden from view inside a living body, many people think of bones as fixed and inert. However, nothing could be further from the truth. Bone is a living tissue that serves as a bank account for "deposits" and "withdrawals" of minerals throughout our lifetimes.

Bone is made of two complementary structural elements: a framework of collagen fibers that provides it with elasticity and resilience (think of that next time your kid falls out of a tree and doesn't break his arm), and minerals deposited around the fibers, which make the bone hard and strong. The architecture of bone tissue can be likened to reinforced concrete, in which steel rods embedded in a solid mixture of cement, gravel and sand allow the rigid structures to withstand a certain amount of stress.

Bone tissue is continuously broken down and rebuilt by two types of cells – osteoclasts, which "chew up" old bone; and osteoblasts, which "build" bone up by encouraging the deposit of minerals on the collagen fiber framework. This dynamic remodeling needs to be perfectly balanced – not too much chewing and not too much building – for our bones to stay healthy. If the balancing act fails, the scaffolding's strength is compromised, an event that can put even the strongest skeleton on the road to bone disease.

The backbone of life-long health

The crucial years for bone formation are childhood and adolescence. In this period of rapid growth – when nothing could be further from our minds than our future state of health – our bodies build up the bone tissue that will quite literally shape the rest of our lives. By the age of 18, girls have acquired up to 90 percent of their bone mass and boys by the age of 20. A gradual build-up continues – out of sight, and out of mind – throughout the next 10 years.

But for bone mass – as in so much else from our youthful days – 30 is the beginning of the end. From our third decade onward, it's all downhill, with bone removal outpacing the building up of new bone tissue. This process increases with age and, in women after menopause, accelerates due to hormonal changes.

Even if – like most people – you paid little attention to your bones during their formative years, there is still hope: you can improve the health of your skeleton at any point in your life. The major lifestyle factors that promote bone health are well established in the medical literature – chiefly, physical activity and healthy nutrition and specifically, an adequate supply of calcium and vitamin D. It is also known which risk factors can cause the most damage to the skeleton: poor diet, a sedentary lifestyle, smoking, alcohol abuse and the long-term use of certain medications such as glucocorticoids and some anti-seizure compounds.

But as you've probably guessed by now, both sets of factors described above are far from being etched in bone – er, that is – stone. In fact, different lifestyle factors affect different people differently, depending on their genes.

Osteoporosis – the silent killer

Anyone who fractures a hip – because of a fall, an automobile accident, or some other event – faces severe pain, as well as a long and difficult process of rehabilitation. For the elderly, however, this trauma is life-threatening; 1 in 2 people who fractures a hip never resumes his or her former lifestyle, and as many as 1 in 4 dies within a year.

Osteoporosis – or "porous bones" – involves bone loss and a steady decline in the skeleton's ability to support the body, a debilitating situation that severely affects independence and overall quality of life. Because bone loss is a hidden process that occurs without symptoms, osteoporosis has been termed "the silent killer."

The scope of the disease is enormous. More than 1.5 million fractures in the United States are associated with osteoporosis each year. According to the National Osteoporosis Foundation, there are an estimated 10 million osteoporosis sufferers in America – 8 million women and 2 million men. In addition, 34 million more are at increased risk for developing the disease due to low bone mass. Altogether, the condition is likely to affect about 44 million people!

Women are at a greater risk for osteoporosis than men because women generally have less bone tissue, particularly if they are small and thin. This gender-specific risk also has a hormonal component; women lose bone faster after menopause. However, it is important to realize that bone health is critical for both women and men. As medical advances allow us to live longer and longer lives, people of both sexes are increasingly susceptible to bone disease.

How genes affect bone health

The fact that genes have a critical effect on bone health is old news. Back in the 1970s and 1980s, studies with twins demonstrated that if one member of a pair of twins had osteoporosis, the other had a higher than average risk of developing the disease as well. Since twins tend to lead similar lifestyles – at least in the earlier part of their lives – the scientists were careful to separate the influence of genes from other, environmental factors that might possibly trigger osteoporosis. To further sharpen the picture, the researchers compared pairs of identical twins, who share all their genes, with pairs of non-identical twins, who, like any two siblings, share only some. The conclusion was straightforward: identical twins were much more likely to have the same risk factors for osteoporosis, such as low bone mass. Clearly, having the same genes was a key factor in determining their risk.

Studies of large population groups are similarly conclusive. Members of certain ethnic communities are at a much greater risk for osteoporosis than others, suggesting that genetic traits linked with race or ethnicity are also associated either with risk factors for bone disease or, conversely, may be associated with protective features that help maintain healthy bones. Thus, for reasons that are still not fully understood, women of Caucasian and Asian ancestry are at a greater risk of osteoporosis than African American and Hispanic women (although the risk in these two latter groups is still significant).

Finally, there's the family connection: daughters of women with osteoporosis have a lower than normal bone mineral content and, after menopause, run a particularly high risk of bone fracture.

Now that the link between genetics and bone health is well established, dozens of research teams around the world are focusing on the role of individual genes. Which genes contribute to which bone properties? How do such genes vary from one person to another, and how are these variants affected by lifestyle factors? Luckily for people who are concerned about maintaining their bone health, some of the results – related to calcium, vitamin D, collagen and inflammation – are already in.

Vitamin D receptor

If you could observe live bone tissue under a microscope over the course of a few days or weeks, you'd see the molecular equivalent of a construction site. Old, worn-out bone cells are continuously being removed, while tiny pieces of new mineral "cement" are being laid down to build new bone. Several dozen genes are involved in this process, but only a few are believed to be major players.

Variation in these "high-ranking" genetic players – the ones that issue commands for bone removal and remodeling – are probably responsible for some people's predisposition toward osteoporosis. For example, a gene variant that triggers increased production of a hormone that issues the command to remove bone cells would play a direct role in speeding the pace of bone loss. In contrast, people with protective gene variants – ones that issue more moderate "commands" – might lose bone mass at a more manageable rate.

In the mid-1980s, scientists began studying a molecular structure called the vitamin D receptor (VDR). The gene that codes for this structure – which has the distinction of being the very first gene ever studied for its effect on bone health – is high ranking indeed; this VDR gene enables cells to respond to vitamin D and calcium, two essential nutrients for normal bone development. As examination of the VDR gene continued, it became clear that variation in this piece of the genetic jigsaw puzzle can have dramatic and serious consequences.

For example, in one study published in 2002, scientists from the China Medical College in Taiwan looked at bone health in 163 postmenopausal women. They found that, for some of the women, the risk of developing osteoporosis in the lower spine was higher than in the other participants by almost 300 percent. Genetic screening revealed that those women with the increased risk had all inherited a certain variant – called Fok1 – of the VDR gene. Since the women didn't differ significantly in other parameters important for bone health, apparently the deterioration of their bones was connected to this version of the gene, which they inherited from both parents.

But how exactly does this variant affect bone health? Basically, by placing an embargo on the skeleton's most important building materials.

Here's how it probably works: the VDR gene is a central player in the absorption of calcium and phosphate from the digestive tract, a process that is dependent on proper metabolism of vitamin D. Certain variants of this gene apparently cause the vitamin D receptor – the molecular "landing pad" that receives this vitamin's chemical message – to be slightly altered in shape. When this happens, it not only affects vitamin D metabolism, it also closes the "gate" against calcium and phosphate, which needs the action of this vitamin to release their payload into bone tissue in sufficient amounts.

But despite the seriousness of this story, there's still a chance for a happy ending: from a practical standpoint, people with detrimental variants of the VDR gene actually seem to have the upper hand when it comes to controlling their bone health through ensuring adequate dietary measures.

That's precisely what was discovered in a study conducted at the Garvan Institute of Medical Research in Sydney, Australia published in 2001. Researchers followed 193 postmenopausal women for 6 years and noted that, while many of the women in the study had potentially harmful variants of the VDR gene, only the ones who consumed little calcium in their diet suffered from significantly increased rates of bone loss in the hip and spine. On the other hand, women who consumed more than 700 milligrams of calcium a day (the amount in 2 to 3 8-ounce servings of milk or yogurt) did not experience accelerated bone loss despite their problematic genes!

But now, let's get back to the coffee-drinking ladies described at the beginning of this chapter. The VDR gene, it appears, also affects the response of bone tissue to caffeine. The women of the coffee club lost bone mass faster if they had a certain variant of the VDR gene. Women without this gene variant also lost bone, but not nearly so fast, despite a heavy coffee habit.

So wake up! If your genes reveal that caffeine puts you at an increased risk of osteoporosis, you would do well to think twice about ordering that second double espresso.

But what if your gene test gives you the opposite result – informing you that you don't have the VDR gene variant that will affect your bone health if you drink large quantities of caffeine? Does this mean you can throw caution to the wind, drinking as much coffee as you want while thanking your lucky Starbucks®? Unfortunately, not quite. While the presence of gene variants increasing your risk of disease is always a call for action, there is no excuse for complacency. Your health is affected by dozens of genes, many still to be understood, so that the absence of one "risky" gene variant can never serve as a license for unsound or unhealthy lifestyle choices.

Collagen building blocks

As with any construction process, it's important that bone rebuilding proceeds in an orderly fashion – with all the proper proteins, minerals and other materials getting to the right place, at the right time and in the right amounts. Unfortunately, this is not always the case, and your genes are once again at the center of the action.

Certain gene variants slightly alter the rebuilding of bone. That's apparently what happens in people with variants of the gene called COL1A1 ("coll-one-ā-one"). The COL1A1 gene is responsible for the production of type 1 collagen, the major protein from which bone is made. People with a certain variant of the COL1A1 gene tend to have lower bone mass and are at an increased risk of fractures. It's unknown how this variant – called Sp1G>T – produces its effect, but according to one theory, it builds up one of the ingredients of collagen at the expense of others, throwing off the "recipe" and adversely affecting bone quality.

The Sp1G>T variant occurs at different rates of prevalence among ethnic groups, and it has not been found at all in Korean, Chinese or Japanese populations, where the incidence of osteoporosis is lower than in Caucasians. This highlights the complex nature of diet-gene relationships. No one gene variant is responsible for a person's susceptibility to osteoporosis, and needs to be studied together with nutritional and lifestyle information.

The good news is that it's easy to compensate for this gene variant's adverse effect. Like the VDR variants described above, Sp1G>T causes concern only when the person bearing this genetic variant does not consume enough calcium. What is more, a calcium-rich diet can actually neutralize this gene variant's osteoporosis-promoting activity. There-fore, knowing the exact kind of COL1A1 gene you have – whether it is the "normal" type or the Sp1G>T variant – allows you to set your pri-orities and make sound nutritional choices for optimal bone health.

A word of caution about calcium. It is possible to get too much cal-cium, so be sure to match your calcium intake to your genotype before deciding that "if some is good, more must be better!"

Inflammation and bone

The word "inflammation" usually brings up images of red or swollen soft tissue, especially skin. But healthy bone tissue also experiences in-flammation on a regular basis – in fact, meticulously controlled inflam-mation is part of the body's natural cycle of bone renewal. However, when the inflammation process is not so well controlled – as in the case of chronic inflammation – more bone is destroyed than is built up. The result of this "inflammation overload" is weakened bone structure and, ultimately, osteoporosis. And when inflammation goes wrong, you can bet the cause is, at least in part, genetic.

Among the inflammatory genes that have been shown to affect bone health are TNF-alpha, IL1 and IL6. These genes produce inflammatory substances that play an important role in bone turnover and come in several versions that have different effects on bone. One variant of TNF-alpha – referred to as -308G>A – has been associated with an increased risk of osteoporosis. In contrast, an IL6 gene variant – called -174G>C – has been found to protect postmenopausal women against bone loss.

A word of caution: if your personal genetic screening shows that you have the protective variant mentioned above, this does not give you the green light to neglect your bones, especially because the effects pro-duced by different genes are far from fully understood. On the other hand, if you don't have this protective variant, or if you have gene variants associated with an increased risk of chronic inflammation in the bone, your mission – as well as your menu – should be clear. Adjust your diet to include substantial amounts of inflammation-fighting food (see text box "Anti-inflammatory food fight," p. 45), and you'll be one step ahead in the fight against bone disease.

ARE YOU AT RISK FOR OSTEOPOROSIS?

To get an idea about your risk of osteoporosis, consider the following:

▶ **FAMILY HISTORY**
  - Do you have a first-degree relative with osteoporosis – a parent, brother or sister? A family history of osteoporosis suggests that you are at increased risk for developing this disorder.
  - Do you have other close relatives with the disease or with a history of fractures?
  - For all your relatives with osteoporosis, consider their diet and lifestyles – both now and during the crucial bone-formative years of childhood and adolescence. If they developed osteoporosis despite having generally consumed adequate amounts of calcium and vitamin D and engaged in physical exercise, chances are there is a genetic predisposition to this disease in your family that will require you to be extra diligent about what you do to promote healthy bone.

▶ **GENETIC SCREENING**
  - Did genetic screening reveal that you have gene variants associated with impaired bone health?

▶ **BONE DENSITY**
  - Have your bone scans indicated subnormal bone density?

▶ **ETHNICITY**
  - Are you Caucasian or Asian? These ethnicities are at particularly high risk for developing osteoporosis, although all ethnicities appear to be at risk if other lifestyle choices are not managed in ways that promote strong bone formation and bone mass retention.

••• *continued* •••

ARE YOU AT RISK FOR OSTEOPOROSIS? *(continued)*

▸ **BODY TYPE**
- Are you thin and small-boned? Individuals, particularly women, with this body type have been found to be at increased risk for developing osteoporosis.

▸ **SMOKING**
- Do you smoke? Smoking has been linked to accelerated bone loss and development of osteoporosis.

▸ **PHYSICAL ACTIVITY**
- Do you regularly engage in weight-bearing exercise? (See text box "Weight-bearing exercise", p. 98)
- Have you been immobilized for a long time? Long-term movement restriction weakens the bones.

▸ **DIETARY HABITS**
- Do you regularly eat foods that are known to promote strong bones? (See text box "Foods that promote bone health", p. 98)
- Do you drink more than three cups of coffee or other caffeine-containing beverages a day? (See text box "Sources of caffeine", p. 96) In people with certain variants of the VDR gene, this practice may increase the risk of bone loss.
- Do you consume more than a moderate amount of alcohol each day? Heavy drinking has been linked to an increased risk for developing osteoporosis (see text box "What is moderate drinking?" p. 37).

▸ **MEDICAL HISTORY**
- Do you suffer from a systemic disease that affects the bone, such as hyperthyroidism or hyperparathyroidism, or from a gastrointestinal inflammatory disorder that decreases nutrient absorption, such as celiac disease, Crohn's disease or ulcerative colitis?
- Do you have a history of fractures?
- Are you taking medications known to weaken bones, such as corticosteroids?

The questions above are intended only as a general guide. To assess your risk of osteoporosis you will need to consult your health care practitioner, who may order a bone scan or other tests.

Taking charge of your bone health the gene-smart way

The advice in this section is meant for everyone, but it's particularly relevant for you if your genes put you at an increased risk for osteoporosis. By knowing your genetic profile, you can identify those recommendations that make the most sense for you and prioritize accordingly.

CALCIUM

An adequate supply of calcium in the diet is a must for healthy bones, yet many people do not consume enough of this vital nutrient. Our need for calcium is greatest during childhood and adolescence, as well as, for women, during pregnancy and breast-feeding. Postmenopausal women and middle-aged men also need a regular supply. And, of course, certain gene variants increase the body's need for dietary calcium (see text box "Daily requirements for calcium," at right).

Ideally, your daily calcium needs should be met by eating calcium-rich foods you enjoy rather than by taking supplements. The average adult needs to consume at

DAILY REQUIREMENTS FOR CALCIUM	
Calcium requirements vary with age	
Age	**Daily amount in milligrams**
Birth–6 months	210
6 months–1 year	270
1–3	500
4–8	800
9–13	1300
14–18	1300
19–50	1000
51–70	1200
70 or older	1200
Pregnant & lactating ≥ 18 years	1000

Source: Dietary Reference Intakes for Calcium, National Academy of Sciences, 1997.

least 1,000 mg of calcium daily, which you can get from 4 eight-ounce glasses of milk or containers of yogurt. However, if you're not routinely meeting your calcium needs through your diet, taking a calcium supplement is a good way to fill this nutritional gap. Rather than taking the entire 1,000 mg dose at one time, take doses of 500 mg or less – it appears that calcium is best absorbed as the smaller dose.

VITAMIN D

Vitamin D, which is essential for the absorption and deposition of calcium and phosphorus in bones and teeth, can be obtained through our diet, but it is also manufactured in the skin in response to sun exposure. Ultraviolet light from the sun converts pro-vitamin D into vitamin D in the skin. According to noted vitamin D researcher Michael Holick, MD, PhD, 10 to 15 minutes of sun exposure twice a week can supply enough vitamin D to meet the needs of most people.

There's a caveat here, however: the benefit you derive from sun exposure depends on the strength of the sun's rays and the absence of significant cloud cover or air pollution. The 10- to 15-minute recommendation applies to clear sunny days during those times of year when the sun is closest to the earth, which in the US, is typically spring through fall. Longer and/or more frequent exposures are needed when the sun is weak. Also, be aware that sunscreen blocks the ultraviolet rays needed to make vitamin D in the skin. Of course, sunscreen is an important precaution against skin cancer, so a good compromise might be to expose your skin to the sun for 10 to 15 minutes and then apply sunscreen.

For housebound people, as well as people who live in cold climates, obtaining vitamin D through sun exposure is a real challenge. Under these circumstances, foods fortified with vitamin D become particularly important. Check product labels; while milk is frequently fortified with vitamin D, not all dairy products are fortified. The typical level of fortification is 10 micrograms of vitamin D (also expressed as 400 International Units, or IU), which is the recommended level for people over 2 years of age. In addition to dairy products, cod liver oil and oil from the livers of other cold water fatty fish also contain vitamin D.

Vitamin D is a fat-soluble vitamin, which means the amounts that exceed your body's needs can be stored in fat tissues rather than removed from the body. Therefore, if you are consuming excessive amounts of this vitamin – if, for example, you're eating the recommended servings of dairy products, taking a multivitamin and using cod liver oil to increase your omega-3 fat intake – it's possible to get too much of a good thing. This is not a reason to panic – just be aware of the potential for excess and use common sense.

EXERCISE
Physical activity is crucial for a healthy skeleton, but all exercise is not created equal when it comes to bone health. In order to strengthen your bones, physical activity must be weight-bearing, meaning that it forces you to work against gravity. (Incidentally, this means that swimming, which is excellent for cardiovascular health, does little to build bone.) Good bone-building activities include walking, hiking, jogging, stair climbing, weight training, tennis and dancing (see text box "Weight-bearing exercise," p. 98).

INFLAMMATION
Knowing the status of your inflammatory gene variants is key to maintaining bone health. This is because excessive activity of genes involved in inflammation may lead to accelerated bone loss. If your gene variants put you at high risk for chronic inflammation, make sure to include plenty of anti-inflammatory foods in your diet (see text box "Anti-inflammatory food fight," p. 45).

ALCOHOL
Numerous studies have shown that heavy drinking increases the risk of bone loss and fractures – and not just because it increases the chances of falling! Alcohol promotes inflammation, which has been linked to decreased bone density. Therefore, by overindulging in drink, you increase your chances of having fragile bones that are easily broken.

SMOKING

Smoking is bad for your health in every respect, and bone health is no exception. It interferes with calcium absorption and, in women, often hastens menopause which, in turn, accelerates bone loss.

CAFFEINE

People with certain genetic profiles need to limit their intake of caffeine in order to protect their bones (see text box "Sources of caffeine," below).

SOURCES OF CAFFEINE

▶ **Sources**

Caffeine is a naturally occurring substance that acts as a stimulant to the central nervous system and promotes the excretion of urine. The obvious culprits to be aware of are coffee, colas and "energy drinks." Tea also contains caffeine. If you need to reduce your intake of caffeine, keep in mind the following:

- The standard cup of coffee is only 6 ounces, but most of us drink coffee by the mug, often several mugs a day. The amount of caffeine in an average 12-ounce mug of coffee is close to 200 milligrams.

- Compared to coffee, colas actually have only about 1/4 the amount of caffeine per ounce of beverage, but we tend to drink them in large amounts. Some light-colored soft drinks, such as Mountain Dew® and Mello Yello®, contain as much caffeine as the darker-colored colas. And remember, diet colas aren't the answer when cutting down on caffeine – they have the sugar removed, not the caffeine. If you're looking to reduce your caffeine intake from colas, choose the caffeine-free varieties or some of the light-colored soft drinks that are free of caffeine.

- Look for the terms guarana and maté, popular ingredients of "energy drinks" – they mean added caffeine.

••• *continued* •••

SOURCES OF CAFFEINE *(continued)*

- Tea is a source of caffeine, but it has only 1/3 to 1/2 the caffeine content of an equivalent amount of coffee.

- Chocolate has gotten some bad press for its caffeine content, but it's actually not so bad if consumed in reasonable quantities. You'd have to eat an entire 6-ounce bag of semi-sweet chocolate chips to equal the amount of caffeine in a 6-ounce cup of coffee! It's definitely possible, but not daily (we hope).

The table below lists the caffeine content of several popular beverages.

Beverage	Caffeine in milligrams
Energy drinks, 8.3 ounces	255
Coffee, brewed, 6 ounces	105
Coffee, decaffeinated, brewed, 6 ounces	0–2
Coffee, instant, 6 ounces	55
Mountain Dew®, 12 ounces	55
Cola, 12 ounces	30–45
Tea, 6 ounces	35
Tea, herbal, 6 ounces	0
Sprite®, 12 ounces	0

Source: USDA National Nutrient Database for Standard Reference — Release 18, www.ars.usda.gov.

BODY WEIGHT

In terms of bone health, a heavier physique is actually beneficial because it makes every step you take a form of weight-bearing exercise! Obviously, this does not mean that you should aim to be overweight. On the other hand, if you are particularly slim and petite, you should pay special attention to the bone-building recommendations listed below.

WEIGHT-BEARING EXERCISE

Strong bones are just one of the many health benefits of physical activity. Adults should engage in at least 30 minutes — and children in at least 60 minutes — of moderate physical activity on most, but preferably all, days of the week (see boxes "Exercise advice" p. 132 and "Tips to keep you exercising," p. 135).

Weight-bearing activities, in particular, force our muscles and bones to work against gravity, which makes them stronger. Walking is the most readily-available weight-bearing activity for most people.

Examples of other weight-bearing activities include:

▶ Baseball
▶ Basketball
▶ Dancing
▶ Field hockey
▶ Hiking
▶ Jogging
▶ Jumping rope
▶ Karate
▶ Push-ups
▶ Racquetball
▶ Running
▶ Soccer
▶ Softball
▶ Stair climbing
▶ Tae kwon do
▶ Tennis
▶ Walking
▶ Weight-lifting

FOODS THAT PROMOTE BONE HEALTH

The major nutrients that promote bone health are calcium, vitamin D, phosphorus, magnesium and vitamin K. Many trace minerals — such as boron, copper, fluoride, iron, manganese and zinc — are also needed for healthy bones. Sources of these nutrients and trace minerals include:

••• *continued* •••

FOODS THAT PROMOTE BONE HEALTH *(continued)*

▸ **Calcium**
- Dairy products (choose low-fat or skim dairy products whenever possible) — low-fat or nonfat milk, natural cheese, yogurt
- Dark green leafy vegetables — bok choy, broccoli, collard greens, mustard greens, spinach, turnip greens
- Almonds
- Canned fish with soft bones — salmon, sardines
- Calcium-fortified foods — breads, cereals, cottage cheese, non-dairy beverages (soy, rice and nut "milks" with added calcium), orange and other 100 percent fruit juices with added calcium, soy beverages, tofu made with calcium sulfate

▸ **Vitamin D**
Few foods contain vitamin D naturally, but those that do include:
- Egg yolks
- Fatty fish
- Fish liver oils

Certain common foods are fortified with vitamin D, such as:
- Milk
- Butter
- Margarine
- Some fortified cereals

▸ **Phosphorus**
- Cereal grains
- Meat
- Milk and milk products
- Nuts
- Protein-rich foods in general

▸ **Magnesium**
- Bananas
- Chocolate
- Dark green vegetables
- Legumes
- Nuts
- Seeds
- Whole grains, including brown rice

▸ **Vitamin K**
- Cruciferous vegetables (broccoli, Brussels sprouts, cabbage, cauliflower)
- Egg yolk
- Green leafy vegetables
- Milk
- Tomatoes

▸ **Trace minerals**
- Dried beans and peas
- Liver
- Nuts
- Whole grains, including brown rice

Source: USDA National Nutrient Database for Standard Reference - Release 18, available at www.ars.usda.gov.

Genetic testing for bone health

Scientific studies have already linked a number of genes involved in bone health with various aspects of diet and lifestyle. The table below lists genes that at present are commonly included in genetic screening. Numerous additional genes are being studied and are expected to be incorporated into future genetic tests.

GENE TESTING FOR BONE HEALTH			
Area of gene's action	Gene name	Gene variant	Major areas of diet and lifestyle that interact with gene variants
Calcium and vitamin D metabolism	Vitamin D receptor (VDR)	TaqI BsmI FokI	• Calcium, especially from dairy foods • Vitamin D • Caffeine • Body weight • Exercise
Collagen synthesis	Collagen type 1 alpha-1 (COL1A1)	Sp1G>T	• Calcium • Vitamin D • Caffeine • Body weight • Exercise
Maintenance of blood calcium levels	Calcitonin receptor (CALCR)	Pro463Leu	• Calcium • Vitamin D
Bone remodeling Inflammation	Interleukin-6 (IL6)	-174G>C -634G>C	• Foods high in omega-3 fatty acids, eg., oily fish such as salmon, flaxseeds and flaxseed oil, walnuts and walnut oil, canola • Body weight • Exercise
	Tumor necrosis factor alpha (TNF-alpha)	-308G>A	

Chapter 7

. . . .

Genes and Body Weight

When we hear people say they can't seem to lose any weight no matter how much they try, it's hard not to be judgmental. We may not say this out loud, but at least some of us are probably wondering: are they really trying hard enough? Or are they perhaps too lazy or weak-willed to shed those pounds? If you are one of these skeptics, consider the following.

In a study published in 2000, researchers from Charles University in Prague, Czech Republic, recruited 14 pairs of female identical twins – all obese – into a hospital, where they were put on a very-low-calorie diet. Throughout the month-long study, the women were closely supervised – they had no chance to raid the fridge or make midnight trips to the corner store. Still, despite the fact that the women were all fed an identical calorie-restricted diet, the results were dramatically different: some lost only 13 pounds (6 kg), while others slimmed down by 26 (12 kg) – in other words, some lucky women enjoyed literally double the rate of weight-loss success.

Interestingly, while there were dramatic differences between different pairs of twins, the difference within each individual pair was far less substantial. Since identical twins have identical genes, this brings us to an obvious conclusion: people with certain genetic profiles lose weight much easier than others. For those eager to lose pounds, this is certainly frustrating news.

The example above is only one of many studies indicating that the tendency to gain weight – and to hold onto it for dear life – is not only about our lifestyle choices but is also embedded in our genes. Compared to the general population, the risk of becoming obese is on average 2 to 3 times higher for an individual with a family history of obesity. And the greater the obesity, the greater the risk: for someone who has first-degree relatives – parents, brothers or sisters – with a body mass index greater than 45 (see text box "Check your body mass index," p. 103), the risk soars to 7 or 8 times the normal level. Of course, family members share not only similar genes, they also make similar dietary and lifestyle choices, but genes surely contribute their part.

So much for the social stigma that follows the overweight like a size XL shadow. Just as some of us are naturally good at math while others tend toward verbal skills, in the same vein – some of us are slim, while others have a tendency to carry too much body weight on our frames. Part of this tendency can be explained by genetically-driven mechanisms that conspire to keep our body weight within a narrow range and resist our best efforts at weight loss.

We're not saying it's okay to be fat – it's not. Excess body fat is unhealthy and predisposes you to a number of chronic, debilitating diseases. What we are saying is that, if you're a weight-challenged individual, there's almost certainly some underlying genetic cause.

This does not suggest you should sit back, relax and just blame your genes for an overly filled-out physique. As we ponder our expanding waistlines, there is no denying that diet and lifestyle are significant contributing factors. Still, genetic awareness opens up new possibilities by helping us pinpoint the personal method that may be most effective in keeping our weight down. By modifying your diet and lifestyle choices so that they match your particular genes, you should be able to make significant progress toward achieving a healthy weight.

Emerging research is already beginning to help people prone to being overweight understand the challenges they face. In this chapter, we describe state-of-the-art nutritional genomics research having to do with weight management.

CHECK YOUR BODY MASS INDEX

A common measure for assessing healthy weight is the body mass index, or BMI, which is calculated from your height and weight.

▶ A healthy body weight is defined as having a BMI of 18.5 to less than 25.

▶ Overweight is defined as a BMI of 25 or more.

▶ Obese is defined as a BMI of 30 or more.

▶ BMI is a convenient shorthand for defining overweight and obesity, but it is not an absolute measure because the real health issue is fat, not weight. Thus, some people in the "normal" BMI range may have lots of fat and little muscle, which is not a healthy situation, while bodybuilders with lots of muscle and little fat are not endangering their health even though they have a high BMI.

▶ To evaluate your BMI, see the chart on the next page.

It's Not Just Your Genes!

BMI	19	20	21	22	23	24	25	26	27	28	29	30	31	32	33	34	35
ADULT BMI CHART																	
Height	Weight in Pounds																
4'10"	91	96	100	105	110	115	119	124	129	134	138	143	148	153	158	162	167
4'11"	94	99	104	109	114	119	124	128	133	138	143	148	153	158	163	168	173
5'0"	97	102	107	112	118	123	128	133	138	143	148	153	158	163	168	174	179
5'1"	100	106	111	116	122	127	132	137	143	148	153	158	164	169	174	180	185
5'2"	104	109	115	120	126	131	136	142	147	153	158	164	169	175	180	186	191
5'3"	107	113	118	124	130	135	141	145	152	158	163	169	175	180	186	191	197
5'4"	110	116	122	128	134	140	145	151	157	163	169	174	180	186	192	197	204
5'5"	114	120	126	132	138	144	150	156	162	168	174	180	186	192	198	204	210
5'6"	118	124	130	136	142	148	155	161	167	173	179	186	192	198	204	210	216
5'7"	121	127	134	140	146	153	159	166	172	178	185	191	198	204	211	217	223
5'8'	125	131	138	144	151	158	164	171	177	184	190	197	203	210	216	223	230
5'9"	128	135	142	149	155	162	169	176	182	189	196	203	209	216	223	230	236
5'10"	132	139	146	153	160	167	174	181	188	195	202	209	216	222	229	236	243
5'11"	136	143	150	157	165	172	179	186	193	200	208	215	222	229	236	243	250
6'0"	140	147	154	162	169	177	184	191	199	206	213	221	228	235	242	250	258
6'1"	144	151	159	166	174	182	189	197	204	212	219	227	235	242	250	257	265
6'2"	148	155	163	171	179	186	194	202	210	218	225	233	241	249	256	264	272
6'3"	152	160	168	176	184	192	200	208	216	224	232	240	248	256	264	272	279
	Healthy weight						Overweight					Obese					

Source: Dietary Guidelines for Americans 2005, available at www.health.gov/dietaryguidelines/dga2005/document/html/chapter3.htm

Obesity and disease risk

Obesity is more than unhealthy – it's life threatening. In the 1930s, American insurance companies, trying to identify those people who would be most likely to cash in on life insurance policies, decided that a high body mass index (see text box "Check your body mass index," p. 103) – was the best predictor. A ratio of body weight to height, body mass index (BMI) is considered high if it is 25 or above.

Because of the many chronic diseases associated with being overweight, particularly type 2 diabetes, obese people tend to die at a younger age than the general population. When the BMI rises to 35, the incidence of diabetes skyrockets; for such individuals, the risk of contracting this disease is 40 to 90 times greater than for those with a BMI of 22.

Obesity also increases the risk of heart disease, stroke, certain forms of cancer, joint problems and a number of breathing disorders. More than 75 percent of high blood pressure cases are reported to be directly attributed to obesity. If rates continue to rise in accordance with current trends, obesity will soon overtake smoking as the leading risk factor for mortality in the United States. It looks like those Depression-era insurance companies had the right idea!

Obesity in the United States

Take a look at Fig 7-1 to really get a feel for the rapid rise in obesity in the US between 1991 and 2004. In no state did the obesity rate of the population reach 20 percent or more in 1991, and only 4 states reached the point where 15-19 percent of the population was obese. By 2004, only 4 states had an obesity rate *less than 20 percent* and each of those states had at least a 15 percent obesity rate!

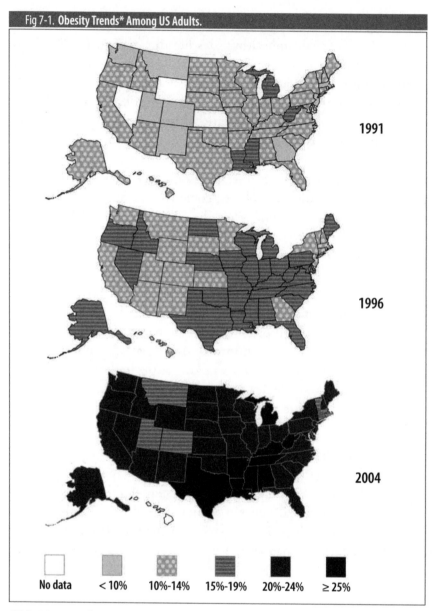

Fig 7-1. Obesity Trends* Among US Adults.

1991

1996

2004

No data   < 10%   10%-14%   15%-19%   20%-24%   ≥ 25%

*BMI ≥30, or ~ 30 lbs. overweight for 5′ 4″ person.
Source: The CDC online at: www.cdc.gov/nccdphp/dnpa/obesity/trend/maps/index.htm

"Thrifty genes" – an evolutionary perspective

Obesity is hardly a new problem: Hippocrates – the ancient Greek physician whose Hippocratic Oath stands as a code of ethics for modern-day physicians – advised the obese to "eat only once a day and take no baths and sleep on a hard bed and walk naked as long as possible." Weight-loss advice has evolved quite a bit in the past 2 millennia! Still, despite medical advances, the problem has soared. Why?

Part of the explanation is simple: we move too little and we eat too much. In industrialized societies, little or no physical labor is needed to fulfill our daily needs. When we require something, we no longer walk to local shops; instead we drive over to a one-stop convenience store or shop online. With more leisure time, both children and adults are watching unprecedented amounts of television or surfing the 'Net. Food is readily available and affordable.

And then, of course, in today's world, junk food is everywhere. Even if you manage to banish unhealthy food products from your home, the message will still sneak in through tantalizing ads designed to make sane people crave insanely inappropriate foods.

Despite this laundry list of society's ills, the fact remains that not everybody gains weight equally. Some people (and we all secretly envy people like this) never exercise and eat as much as they want and still don't gain weight. Excess weight develops only when these practices are combined with the right – or, rather "wrong" – kind of genes.

In chapter 5 we discussed diabetes, a problem closely related to obesity. There, we mentioned the "thrifty gene" theory, which states that our genetic make-up, which has changed little over the past 50,000 years or so, was honed for survival in near-famine conditions – a situation that is certainly at odds with our modern life of plenty. For our hunter-gatherer forefathers, the search for food was a back-breaking, time-consuming activity. It was also risky – hunter-gatherers could not always provide enough food to meet the caloric requirements of the tribe. Under these circumstances, laying on the fat provided a distinct advantage because it allowed people to stockpile food energy that could be called upon during times of scarcity.

The same genes that ensured our forefathers' survival in times of famine may be the genes that predispose modern man to obesity: these genes add extra pounds to our waistline and are never shed because food is abundant year round. According to this theory, people with more of the once-advantageous "thrifty" genes are at a particular disadvantage in an environment where storing away excess calories on your body is no longer necessary.

"Thrifty" genes can cause entire ethnic groups to gain weight in response to a change in their lifestyle. Before the arrival of Europeans, Australian Aboriginal tribes did well on a low-fat, high-fiber diet consisting mostly of slow-release carbohydrates such as certain roots and berries. These food sources were gathered during long treks through the outback. Then, many years ago, this same population was fenced in on government-approved reserves and given a steady supply of Western-style food and drink. Although the Aborigines are now free to live wherever they choose, many still make their homes in the reserves and have lost touch with the tradition of cross-country treks – like the rest of us, they prefer to pick up their food at the store. The sad result is that the Aboriginal population, once quite slim, is now worse off in terms of obesity rates than the rest of the country: 24 percent of Aboriginal males and 27 percent of Aboriginal women are classified as obese, compared with 19 percent for the rest of the Australian adult population.

Weighing the genetic evidence

The link between genes and obesity has been established since the 1960s and 1970s. In those early studies, the weight of adopted children was compared with the weight of both their adoptive and biological parents, to see to what extent body weight is determined by "nature"

– that is, genes – and how much by "nurture" – nutrition and lifestyle. In the vast majority of these studies, nature won out; adopted children were more likely to have a BMI similar to that of their biological parents rather than their adoptive parents.

Similar evidence for the role of genetics comes from twin studies, which are particularly popular in obesity research. Scientists all over the world have looked at thousands of twin pairs, and the conclusion is unequivocal: identical twins have a much greater chance of having similar weights, even when reared apart, compared with non-identical twins.

Our genetic profile influences more than just our tendency to stay slim or become obese. It also has a significant impact on our chances for long-term weight-loss success. After all, going on a diet is not all that difficult. As Mark Twain stated about quitting smoking, "It's easy; I've done it many times." The hard part is stabilizing the results; unfortunately, even when people manage to lose weight, most gain it back.

Such "yo-yo" dieting – in which weight is gained, then lost, then gained again – may be caused by a gene-based mechanism described in what scientists refer to as the "lipostat theory." Like the thermostat that controls the temperature in our home, our body's lipostat mechanism is thought to monitor and regulate our energy expenditure, helping keep our body mass stable by balancing the fat we burn against the fat we store ("lipids" is a scientific term for fat; "lipostat" could be loosely translated as "fat-o-stat"). According to the theory, in overweight people, the lipostat may be broken or set at a level that's too high. When the body "reads" the lipostat, it gets an incorrect message and, as a result, is stimulated to eat more than it actually needs.

Beyond its role in gaining weight, the proposed lipostat mechanism apparently has a part to play in weight loss as well, and may be one of the reasons that some people find it so difficult losing weight or keeping the weight off after it's been lost. When you embark on a low-calorie diet, the lipostat – which, as you recall, is believed to be responsible for managing energy expenditure – slows down the body's metabolic processes because there is less energy to burn. In individuals with certain genetic profiles, the body responds to the lowered calorie intake by burning up the available food energy in a particularly sluggish manner.

At the same time, the theory goes, the lipostat sends that all-too-familiar "hunger" message to the brain. This message is turned up – loud – and becomes an "alarm," demanding that the body eat…more…NOW! It's as if the body is actively resisting weight loss and attempting to return to its previous, heavier weight.

The lipostat theory offers an interesting explanation for the current obesity epidemic. Thinking about it in terms of human evolution, there may always have been people with "broken" lipostats whose genes predisposed them to constant, insatiable hunger. In the ancient world, however, where intense effort was required to procure enough food for survival, over-eating was simply not an option. Today, food is readily available; if our lipostat "tells" us we are hungry, all we have to do is walk to the refrigerator – again, and again, and again.

Of obese mice and men

One of the key genes that may be involved in the lipostat mechanism was discovered thanks to an obese mouse born in a US laboratory in the 1950s. The mouse had not been intentionally bred to be obese, it just happened to be born this way, but researchers seized this unusual opportunity to study obesity. They found that the mouse consistently passed obesity on to some of its offspring, which meant that the trait was somehow embedded in the genes. The obese mice ate almost continuously, weighed twice as much as normal mice, had a slower metabolism and became less active as they got older. It wasn't until about 40 years later that another group of scientists identified the gene responsible for this mouse's obesity. They showed that this gene, which is also present in humans, produces a hormone that, among its other functions, informs the brain about the body's energy stores and controls appetite.

The researchers called the hormone "leptin," from the Greek word *leptos*, meaning "thin." Mice with fully functioning leptin-producing genes were trim and slim. In contrast, mice that produced leptin in insufficient quantities became obese. And in an experiment that electrified obesity researchers around the world, when the obese mice received an injection of leptin, they lost almost half of their excess weight within a month, started to eat less and seemed to experience no side effects.

The mouse is amazingly similar to humans genetically so, for a while, it looked as if the problem of obesity was about to be solved – at least in mice. "Before" and "after" photos of obese mice now thin from leptin injections made headlines in all the papers, and expectations for an anti-obesity drug for humans ran high.

In human trials, however, these hopes started to falter. Many obese people were found to have enough leptin already, so giving them more of this hormone was not particularly helpful. In addition, some of the subjects were apparently, to some extent, immune to leptin's effect. These findings led to a new line of inquiry, in which scientists attempted to reveal the chain of events leading to leptin response in the brain, and increase the efficiency of this process.

All this research has led to an understanding that, on the genetic level, obesity is an extremely complex problem: there are many, many genes that contribute to the condition. In fact, hundreds of genes could be involved in regulating weight, including genes responsible for the control of appetite, generation of fat tissue, metabolism of the food we eat and other aspects of body function.

Weight-loss genes

Among the hottest studies in nutritional genomics are those seeking to identify specific genes contributing to obesity and to understand how they work. Once that is achieved, the potential for action is great: it may be possible to create drugs that will modify the function of these genes. Better still, the findings may lead to non-pharmaceutical strategies that will allow us to compensate for our genetic limitations by adopting appropriate dietary and lifestyle measures.

Scientists have already identified several genes that play a role in our varying ability to achieve and maintain a healthy body weight. These genes come in several versions, and some people get the raw deal of having the version that makes them more prone to weight gain.

In one research project, scientists analyzed the report of the Quebec Overfeeding Study, in which 12 pairs of young male identical twins were subjected to a dietary experiment. Unlike the underfed female twins in the Czech study described at the beginning of this chapter, these Canadian men stayed in a closed dormitory at Laval University for 3 months and ate 1,000 calories a day more than their usual diet.

Unlike the early-days twin studies – in which researchers sought to establish the relative importance of genes to body weight – here the goal was to identify specific genes involved in the weight gain process. The Canadian researchers zeroed in on the beta-2 adrenergic receptor, one of the genes already known to play a role in regulating energy balance and fat breakdown. Sure enough, the researchers identified one particular variant, called Gln27Glu, that appeared to be one of those gene versions that may make dieting difficult. While all study subjects gained weight – an average of 17 pounds (8 kg) – twins with the Gln27Glu gene version gained more.

Different versions of the beta-2 adrenergic receptor were also shown to determine to what extent exercise can help an individual lose weight and reduce body fat. In a 2003 study conducted at the same Canadian university, a group of researchers subjected several hundred sedentary people to a cycling regimen 3 times a week. After 20 weeks, the subjects' response to exercise was examined. They found that the women with two copies of one form of the gene, Arg16Arg, responded to the exercise program with a greater loss of body fat compared with those without this gene variant. Such studies may in the future help identify people who can benefit most from a personalized weight-loss program involving lifestyle modifications that include a specific exercise regimen.

Other potential culprits in obesity are genes that play a role in fateful "decisions" about how much energy is burned as heat as opposed to being stored as fat. One of these genes, UCP1 (uncoupling protein 1), comes in several versions, and a number of studies have shown that people with a G version of this gene are prone to obesity and have less success in weight-loss programs than people with another version, the A variant.

Who needs which diet?

The studies described in the previous section help explain why different people respond to the same diet differently. But it's also known that the same person may respond differently to different diets: he or she may lose almost no weight on one diet but quite a bit on another. The next step is to try to figure out why this happens so that every person can be matched to the appropriate weight-loss program.

People who need to watch their weight (and most of us do) often know from experience which foods are particularly "dangerous" in terms of weight gain. Similarly, studies are beginning to identify groups of people that would benefit from one diet as opposed to another. Scientists don't always know which genes are involved, but it's definitely possible to identify specific subgroups that take different paths towards dieting success. For example, Australian researchers recently put two groups of overweight and obese people on two different weight-loss programs, one high in protein and the other high in carbohydrate. While both diets were beneficial, the researchers identified a group of subjects who lost more weight on the high-protein diet: these were the obese people with high levels of fats called triglycerides in their blood.

It's unknown why this diet benefited these people most, and scientists cannot say with certainty whether all people with high triglycerides should adopt a high-protein diet. However, while not a gene-based approach, this study does point in that direction by identifying subsets of people who derive the most benefits from a particular diet. In the future, most if not all studies of this sort will include genetic analysis, and it will be possible to match the optimal diet to genes.

But what about those people who are "resistant" to weight loss? We are talking about people who can't seem to lose substantial amounts of weight no matter what they try. Can we explain this phenomenon from a genetic standpoint? If so, what kind of diet will they be advised to follow? A good first step toward answering these questions would be to do a genetic screening to check whether these individuals have gene variants conferring a resistance to weight loss.

One such gene variant was recently identified. Researchers from the United States and Spain studied different variants of a gene called PLIN that makes a protein (perilipin) controlling the storage of certain fats in cells: it coats fat droplets, protecting them from breakdown. Mice in whom this gene has been disrupted through genetic manipulation break down fat at an increased rate, and these mice are lean, muscular and do not develop diet-induced obesity even when offered an unlimited amount of food. The researchers found that obese people with a gene version called PLIN4(A) tend not to lose weight on low-calorie weight-loss diets. It's unknown why, but researchers speculate that these people have internal mechanisms that give them a tendency toward stable weight regulation, independent of the number of calories they may consume.

If these results are confirmed – and when other genes are discovered that function along the same lines – it may become possible to predict who is going to have difficulty losing weight. Ultimately, this information may help design gene-smart approaches to weight loss that would work best for these individuals. They will need to set lower, more realistic weight-loss goals, and will be advised to focus on other, more manageable aspects of their lifestyle to make sure that, if they can't lose weight, at least everything else they do is healthy.

A matter of taste

While most "obesity genes" have to do with body chemistry, it looks like genes begin to play a role in weight management even before food gets past your mouth. That's because our food choices are dictated by our taste preferences, something that is also influenced by our genes.

Inborn differences in taste were discovered long before genetics became a full-fledged science. In 1931, chemists at DuPont were experimenting with a compound called phenylthiocarbamide, or PTC. A certain amount of the PTC powder, which is not harmful, got into the air and into the scientists' mouths. Some of them exclaimed that it tasted bitter, but the lead investigator, a chemist called Arthur Fox, said he tasted nothing. He started giving PTC crystals to family, friends and colleagues and found that some of them tasted nothing, like himself, while others found it bitter in varying degrees. This discovery led to numerous studies in which scientists tested people's ability to taste PTC. It soon emerged that the differing responses to PTC are the result of a genetic variation.

Today taste researchers are using PTC and another bitter chemical called 6-n-propylthiouracil, or PROP, not only to study the genetics of taste but also to check how different taste perceptions translate into different, weight-determining eating habits. Studies show that in the adult Caucasian population in North America, 30 percent are "taste-blind" to the bitterness of PTC and PROP. Researchers call such individuals "non-tasters," though they are able to taste these chemicals when they're presented at higher than the usual concentrations. The remaining 70 percent are called "tasters," and some of them are "super-tasters." Super-tasters — those lucky individuals who get more swoon from the spoon — are usually more sensitive to various sweet tastes and to fat texture as well. (Being a super-taster can be a mixed blessing, though; given crystals of PTC powder, super-tasters were so overwhelmed by the bitterness that they actually cried out!)

Tasters tend to have more food dislikes and to have an aversion to strong-tasting foods, such as sauerkraut and strong cheeses, and what they choose to eat appears to be different from what non-tasters eat, which ultimately affects body weight.

Taste researchers at Rutgers University, who conducted numerous studies on this topic, have taken the taster/non-taster/super-taster story a step further: they discovered that non-tasters tend to be heavier and have a greater percentage of body fat, while super-tasters tend to be thinner and leaner. For example, in one study of middle-aged women, they found that non-tasters had an average body mass index of 29, while tasters had a body mass index of only 23. In another study, these researchers showed that non-taster preschool children were more likely to enjoy full-fat milk and ate 2 to 3 more servings of fatty foods per day compared with taster boys and girls.

So it looks like food choices are, to some extent, governed by our genes. The sweet tooth is probably at least partly a genetic trait, as is an affinity for fatty food. It's also quite possible that super-tasters tend to eat less, as they get a lot of *mmm*! out of every mouthful, while the non-tasters may have to eat more to satisfy their dull taste buds.

Obesity, diabetes and inflammation

Genetic mechanisms underlying obesity are so complex that they also involve genes having no obvious connection to body fat, such as the genes that code for the body's inflammatory response. Apparently, fat tissue produces inflammatory substances, and according to some theories, these substances may be at least partly responsible for the fact that obese people have an increased risk of type 2 diabetes as well as insulin resistance, a pre-diabetic condition characterized by the cells' reduced sensitivity to the hormone insulin.

One inflammatory substance called TNF-alpha, which is produced primarily in fat tissue, has been specifically associated with type 2 diabetes and insulin resistance as well as obesity. Studies suggest that giving mice TNF-alpha produces insulin resistance, while blocking TNF-alpha can improve insulin sensitivity.

If the theories linking obesity, diabetes and inflammation are supported by further research, it will become critically important to identify obese people with overly active inflammatory genes – for example, those with certain versions of TNF-alpha. These people will be advised to adopt a weight-loss diet that is also anti-inflammatory in order to help avert such serious complications of obesity as insulin resistance and diabetes.

Eating disorders

Eating disorders, such as bulimia and binge eating, have also been shown to be linked to genes. Bulimia was historically considered to be influenced primarily by society's emphasis on thinness and attractiveness. However, only a small number of people exposed to these influences in society develop the full-blown binge-and-purge behavior associated with bulimia.

In the past decade, scientific research has led to a growing awareness that genetics contributes substantially to the tendency towards binge eating. For example, an international team of physicians and scientists from Switzerland, Germany and the United States studied different variants of a gene called melanocortin 4 receptor, believed to be involved in the control of eating behavior. They examined 470 obese men and women and found that 24 obese subjects had a slightly altered version of this gene. Every one of the subjects who carried this variant – 100 percent – reported binge eating. Among obese subjects without the altered gene, only 14 percent reported binge eating.

We are still very far from having practical applications of such findings, and eating disorders are still largely addressed through psychotherapeutic techniques. But as we find out more about the genes governing eating disorders, such knowledge takes away some of the stigma by revealing that binge eating is not just disordered eating, but rather, has a genetic basis. And as we add to our knowledge, we will be able to determine whether these genes can be affected by lifestyle, something that would help pinpoint the most effective strategies for battling eating disorders.

Gene-smart weight control

By placing health above slimness, and by understanding your individual genetic limitations, a comfortable relationship with your body is achievable. As difficult as it may be, it is worth the effort to do what we can to attain – and maintain – a healthy body weight. Even a modest weight loss of 5 to 10 pounds (2 to 4.5 kg) can improve our health and is achievable with good food choices and increased exercise. But remember: realistic weight goals are fundamental, and the "ideal" body image portrayed by the media is, for most of us, simply unattainable.

For those most susceptible to gaining weight, prevention is paramount, as it's much easier to prevent weight gain than to lose weight afterwards. Genetic testing should in the future help us identify people who are most prone to weight gain. In the same manner as we are trying to identify people with a genetic risk of heart disease and advise them to take precautions early, so we will be able to identify people at risk of weight gain and help them prevent it early in life.

In the not-too-distant future, people seeking to lose weight will undergo a genetic screening that will map out the most important of their genes related to body weight, and their diet and exercise options will be constructed accordingly. With a greater knowledge of the genetic causes of obesity, all members of society – not just scientists – may take a critical look at what it means to be overweight and, in so doing, open their eyes to the full range of new possibilities.

In the meantime, below are several strategies for sound weight control. You will, of course, adjust your diet and physical activity to your personal preferences, but the following general guidelines work well for most people:

THE THREE C'S

Pay attention to three C's: (1) Calories you eat, (2) Composition of those calories (macronutrients, such as protein, fat, and carbohydrate) and (3) Control of your portion sizes. Your total daily intake should be made up of approximately 50 percent carbohydrates, 20 percent protein and 30 percent fat (mostly monounsaturated and polyunsaturated) and should be divided into 5 or 6 small meals, as in the following:

▸ A good breakfast with plenty of protein, some fat and minimum carbohydrates.

▸ A mid-morning snack.

▸ Lunch with moderate protein, some fat and more carbohydrates than breakfast.

▸ Protein/fat mid-afternoon snack, such as nuts.

▸ Dinner with some protein, some fat and mostly carbohydrates.

▸ A light snack before bed, if any.

It's Not Just Your Genes!

REGULAR EXERCISE
Combine aerobic exercise 3 days a week with twice-weekly resistance training.

STRIKING A BALANCE
Stay busy and engaged in all your regular activities so that weight loss is not the main thing in your life. If you follow a reasonable diet, as suggested above, you will not be hungry, you'll have enough energy to exercise and, as time passes, you'll gain muscle mass and lose body fat. Even if you think you weigh more than you should according to your bathroom scale, remember: muscle weighs more than fat. Therefore, as the fat melts away, your body size will shrink, even if your total weight doesn't significantly change.

It's tempting to hop on and off the scale while losing weight, but a better way to track your progress is how well your clothes fit. Begin with an outfit that's a bit tight – your "goal clothes" - and try it on again in a couple of weeks. When the clothes fit comfortably, regardless of what your scale registers, congratulate yourself! Then, if additional size reduction is your goal, select a new set of clothes that are a bit tight and continue to eat smart and exercise regularly. Repeat as needed.

Gene-directed weight loss and maintenance is in its early stages, but it is a sound and promising approach. Attaining and maintaining a healthy weight is possibly the single-most important step you can take to improve your overall health, and with it, your longevity and quality of life. Stay tuned!

Chapter 8

The Genetics of Fitness

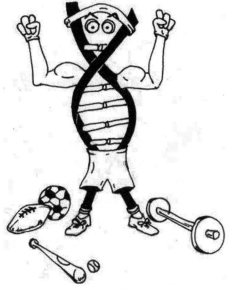

Some people are just born to win. While there's no denying that hard work and perseverance are vital to athletic achievement, some athletes have something more: one or more genes that gives them a leg up on the competition.

A notable example is Eero Mäntyranta. A Finnish cross-country skier who won two gold medals in the 1964 Winter Olympics in Innsbruck, Mäntyranta was born with a rare genetic alteration that increased the ability of his red blood cells to carry oxygen to his muscles. While the others huffed across the icy trail, Mäntyranta could breathe easier, his steady, powerful movements fueled by up to 50 percent more oxygen than his rivals. In Mäntyranta's case, we know the exact cause of his genetic advantage: an alteration in the gene coding for erythropoietin, a hormone made in the kidneys that stimulates the body to produce more red blood cells.

But even when we can't point to a genetic "smoking gun," it is clear that outstanding athletic prowess has – at least in part – a hereditary component. For instance, the famous siblings Venus and Serena Williams – both international tennis stars – may owe their many Wimbledon wins to a family culture that stressed physical fitness. But there's probably also something in their genes that gave their bodies the potential to become outstandingly strong and fast. This "genetic advantage" might have given them the raw material they needed to achieve athletic greatness.

Genetic aspects of athletic performance are also relevant for those who do not aspire to a career in professional sports. Whether you are a "recreational athlete" who participates enthusiastically in a local sports team or a "guilt athlete" who frequents a gym under doctor's (or spouse's) orders, genes affect your every move. In this chapter, we'll tell you what's known about the relationship between genes and physical fitness and what you can expect in the future in this area.

Response to exercise: power vs. endurance

The Mäntyranta-type genetic alteration is exceedingly rare, but there are other gene variants affecting athletic performance that are much more common in the general population.

Here's one example. Usually, athletes tend to be good either at power or at endurance, not both. Data on world-class decathletes – who participate in a grueling collection of 10 different contests – show that those individuals who have the explosive power to perform well in the 100-meter sprint and other short-distance events, do less well in the 1,500 meter race, which requires endurance.

This either/or phenomenon is probably due to several genes that affect power versus endurance. When subjected to the same training regimen, athletes with a genetic profile that marks them as "power" types will increase the bulk of their muscle fibers that provide short-term explosive energy. This energy, however, will be exhausted after running 100 meters. In contrast, for "endurance" types, intensive training will not result in markedly increased muscle bulk; instead, these athletes' muscles will become more efficient, giving them the long-lasting strength they need to propel the body over the finish line after long running, swimming or biking events.

So is there a "P" gene that programs us for power and an "E" gene that ensures endurance? Not exactly. Numerous genes affect our athletic tendencies, and there is nothing "preprogrammed" about their impact; rather, different versions of these genes reveal their influence only if combined with certain types of training. For example, one of the best-studied genes believed to affect our response to exercise is the one coding for ACE, an enzyme involved in the regulation of blood pressure and other body processes. In one variant, the ACE gene is associated with short-term bursts of power. In the other variant, the gene appears to be associated with endurance over the long haul.

In one British study, the ACE gene variants were – quite literally – shown to affect peak performance. The researchers found that elite male mountaineers with a history of ascending beyond 7,000 meters without using supplementary oxygen were far more likely to have the "endurance" variant of the ACE gene than other men who did not climb mountains. In another study by the same researchers, this one focusing on British army recruits, the ACE gene was found to dramatically affect response to exercise. After a 10-week physical training program, the soldiers with two copies of the ACE "endurance" gene variant improved a full 11 times more than the recruits who did not have this gene variant!

But ACE is not the only power-versus-endurance gene. In an Australian study, researchers screened more than 400 elite devotees of 14 different sports – including 50 athletes who had competed in the Olympics – for variants of a gene called ACTN3 (actinin alpha-3). Although the precise function of this gene is not fully understood, ACTN3 is known to produce a protein present in "fast" muscle fibers – those tissues that help sprint athletes produce explosive bursts of speed for short periods of time. Sure enough, sprint athletes, such as short-distance swimmers, track cyclists and speed skaters, were very unlikely to carry the variant that blocked ACTN3 activity. In contrast, among elite endurance athletes – including long-distance cyclists, rowers, cross-country skiers, swimmers and distance track athletes – the incidence of the blocked-activity gene variant was *higher* than in the general population. Apparently, not having a functional ACTN3 protein is an advantage for slow, efficient performance in endurance sport.

The genes for power versus endurance are, of course, only one piece of the puzzle. Other genes that affect the way we respond to exercise are involved in regulating fat and glucose metabolism, controlling the heart and breathing, and affecting post-exercise changes in body composition – in other words, the way in which we "cool down." A recent scientific review lists more than 100 genes linked with response to exercise or sports performance, and many more will likely be identified in the future.

Exercise and its effect on our genes

Genes affect our response to exercise, but the reverse is also true – exercise affects the way genes work. Research suggests that exercise can change the rates at which our genes turn on and off, affecting the speed at which certain proteins are released into the body. Experts in the relationship between genetics and exercise are studying how physical activity can affect the functioning of our genes, resulting in a host of benefits. Among these are an increased sensitivity to insulin, improved blood glucose metabolism, boosting the use of stored fats and a decrease in the creation of fat tissue. They are also examining how different exercise regimens – based on exercise type, intensity, duration and frequency – can affect gene expression and play an important role in the prevention of disease.

If you think you will have to drastically increase your level of physical activity to affect the functioning of your genes, think again: even a single bout of exercise can affect gene function. For example, an Australian study has revealed that the activity of a gene that helps glucose move efficiently from the bloodstream into the cells, increased immediately after a single 1-hour session on a stationary bicycle. This finding might help explain why those with insulin resistance who exercise regularly see considerable improvement in their insulin sensitivity.

Another study, this one conducted by Australian and Canadian researchers, showed that a single 1-hour session of vigorous cycling increased the activity of 2 genes involved in moving fatty acids (broken down fats) into the cell. Therefore, as a result of a simple spin on a stationary bike, it is possible to affect your genes so that your body burns more energy and stores less in the form of fat.

The nutrition connection

As we have seen, exercise can have a major impact on the function of our genes. But to take full advantage of exercise's gene-smart benefits, we first have to prime the pump – with the right kinds of foods. More and more scientific studies are revealing the important role nutrition has to play in the way our genes work – both when we are sedentary and when we engage in exercise.

Anyone who has ever tried to run a marathon (or even a day's errands!) on an empty stomach will not be surprised to hear that physical activity, sports performance and recovery from exercise are enhanced by optimal nutrition. Professional athletes, if they value their contracts, must pay serious attention to the advice they receive from sports nutritionists, who have developed specific expertise in the relationship between food, body chemistry and performance on the playing field. Recreational athletes should also watch what they eat to get the best out of their exercise program and help manage their weight. And, as our genetic knowledge expands, dietary recommendations for both elite and recreational athletes will be increasingly designed with our genes in mind.

In fact, the way physical activity affects our genes may depend on the diet that preceded the exercise. Many of us have heard of "carbo-loading" – a technique in which long-distance runners and cyclists load up on carbohydrate for up to 3 days before a race. What we might not be aware of is that this "loading" is not really about the chocolate crunch cereal – though it sure tastes good. Rather, it is about a compound called glycogen that stores carbohydrate in the muscles and liver. Eating large amounts of carbohydrate on the days before an endurance event makes sure that glycogen stores are as full as they can be. During long races, when energy-producing glucose carried in the blood has been depleted, stored glycogen is summoned into action, turning into glucose that streams into the blood to keep those legs pumping.

To further understand the importance of glycogen, let's look at a study by Danish and American researchers investigating how genes, exercise and diet – particularly the carbohydrate component of our diet – interact. The researchers asked a group of athletes to perform vigorous exercise for 3 hours, 2 days in a row – first after eating a normal diet, and the next day after eating a low-carb diet that reduced the amount of glycogen in their muscles by 60 percent. Though a certain inflammatory response always occurs after exercise, the researchers found that the activity of one gene involved in inflammation soared by up to 300 percent when the athletes had low glycogen stores in their muscles after the low-carb diet. A better illustration for the interrelationship between genes, diet and exercise would be hard to find.

Exercise, genes and your risk of disease

As scientists reach a greater understanding of how genes, exercise and nutrition are all linked together, our personal strategies for healthy living will include individualized, gene-based programs that will tell us not only what to eat, but also how – and how much – to exercise.

We already know that the health benefits of exercise are not distributed evenly throughout the population. Although exercise can help prevent certain diseases, some people may derive greater benefits from physical activity than others. In addition, people respond differently to different types of exercise.

Obviously, a clear understanding of the health benefits that can be derived from physical activity can do wonders for your gym-time motivation. This can be especially valuable if a particular disease – like diabetes or high blood pressure – runs in your family. Here are a few examples of what studies show:

▸ A 2003 study of healthy middle-aged Japanese men and women identified a group of people with a certain variant of the gene called NOS3 who were particularly likely to reduce their blood pressure with the help of physical exercise.

▸ In 2002, Turkish researchers showed that exercise may be particularly helpful in controlling pressure within the eye – a risk factor for glaucoma – if people carry certain variants of the gene called beta-2 adrenergic receptor.

▸ Sedentary lifestyle is a risk factor for diabetes, but, according to a 2003 German study, people with certain variants of the vitamin D receptor gene are at a greater risk than others

▶ In the chapter on heart health, we wrote that people with a certain variant of the APOE gene tend to have higher levels of "bad" cholesterol. However, in 2003, Italian researchers discovered that, in men who cycled 75 to 93 miles (120 to 150 kilometers) a week, cholesterol levels stayed normal even if they had this gene variant.

Gene-savvy personal training?

More studies are needed before it will be possible to create customized exercise programs based on an individual's specific genetic strengths and vulnerabilities. But in the future, genetic screening is expected to play an important role in incorporating exercise into personalized disease prevention. In the meantime, if you are not yet physically active, it's a good idea to increase your level of physical activity. After all, with such a sweeping range of positive health effects, exercise is an excellent way to ensure that you can actualize your genetic potential for good health.

All this discussion of the benefits of exercise brings us to a very big sticking point: compliance with an exercise regimen. Most of us are not training for the Olympics, but even the most dedicated recreational athletes fall off the wagon, letting their pre-paid gym card disappear under the clutter on their desks or turning that oh-so-expensive treadmill into nothing but a convenient place to hang their clothes. Even when we do continue exercising, sometimes boredom sets in, brought on by our frustrating inability to better our time in doing laps in the pool or jogging around the track. Motivation, it would seem, is tied to our sports success – or lack thereof.

Adjusting your exercise regimen to your genetic profile can change all that. By knowing your genetic make-up, you will have the data you need to plan an exercise strategy that will help you improve – in strength, endurance and overall fitness – over a sustained period of time. By putting more energy into a form of exercise in which your body will give you better feedback, you'll feel less tired, you'll recover more quickly and your motivation – and your self-esteem – will rise.

No exercise advice – even advice based on genes – is absolute, and you still need to listen to your body and, if you enjoy a particular type of physical activity, it doesn't matter whether genetically speaking you are gold medal material. Genetic testing will never tell an individual *not* to run a marathon or to participate in any particular sport. But if finding the right exercise regimen is based on experimentation, you'll be more likely to hit on the right form of physical activity for you if you start out closer to the mark. That's the gym of the future.

Genetic screening – an ethical dilemma?

While genetic testing has obvious potential benefits both for recreational and elite athletes, as with all new technologies, it raises the concern of abuse. It's one thing to scan a room of school-age gymnasts and pick out the short, lithe girls that are likely to do well on the uneven parallel bars. It's quite another to use genetic screening to determine who wins a spot on the high school track team. Will genetic screening be used as a way to discriminate against people whose genes don't stack up against the competition?

Probably not, as sports performance is a very complex matter involving dozens of genes that affect various aspects of body physiology, including the regulation of blood flow and pressure, heart rate, clearance of lactic acid and our body's use of oxygen, and many of these are affected by nutrition. Moreover, sports success has a significant psychological component – whatever one's genetic tendencies, it takes a special kind of person to withstand the stress and maintain the discipline necessary to become an outstanding athlete.

However, genetic screening can provide guidance and perhaps help athletes make choices earlier. Young athletes who need to decide upon a certain sport early in their career may still have to experiment with different training regimens and evaluate their performance in different sports. Still, knowing their genetic advantages and disadvantages can give some athletes a better start, helping them make informed decisions rather than proceeding only by trial and error.

Elite athletes are always looking for ways to beat the record by that extra second, and if they have genetic knowledge about their body chemistry, and both their training and their nutrition are individualized and matched to their genes, they can improve their chances to achieve their best possible performance.

When it comes to the interaction between diet, genes and exercise, there's still much to learn, but as the results roll in, it looks like – genetically speaking – it's going to be a great era for sports fans.

Gene-smart nutrition for optimal fitness

Making nutritional choices that best match your genes is a powerful strategy for getting your body to perform at its best, and this is particularly important if you are physically active. Below are a few recommendations, some of them general; others depend on your individual genetic profile. Of course, the specific diet that's right for you will also depend on your preferred type of exercise, as well as its duration and intensity.

MEETING YOUR BODY'S ENERGY AND NUTRITIONAL NEEDS

During times of intensive physical activity, make sure that your diet includes adequate amounts of carbohydrate and protein. These will replenish glycogen stores in your liver and muscles (see "The nutrition connection" on p. 125) and provide the nutrients for building and repairing your tissues. You also need to be eating fats; the right amount of healthy fats – particularly omega-3 fats – can provide energy and help reduce exercise-induced inflammation.

DRINKING SUFFICIENT FLUIDS

Make sure to drink before exercise. If it's warm out, or you are exercising for a long time or at a high intensity, drink during and after exercise as well. You may consider trying sports drinks that contain carbohydrates and electrolytes. Such drinks will provide fuel for your muscles, help maintain blood glucose levels, quench your thirst and decrease the risk of dehydration.

REDUCING OXIDATIVE STRESS
In chapter 4 we noted that, as our bodies produce energy, they also generate destructive molecules called free radicals. During physical activity – when your blood is pumping more, your heart is beating faster, you are breathing more oxygen in and more carbon dioxide out – you produce more energy. As a result, more free radicals are produced.

Free radicals are behind oxidative stress, a condition that is harmful to our tissues and organs. We fight oxidative stress with the help of antioxidants – both those produced naturally in the body and those derived from food. If you happen to be one of those people who has an increased requirement for antioxidants in the diet because your antioxidant genes are not very efficient, this requirement increases even more if you exercise.

The problem with oxidative stress is that it causes no symptoms. If you engage in vigorous physical activity and your antioxidant genes are inefficient – and if, in parallel, you are not giving yourself enough antioxidant support from your diet -- you may be causing yourself slow, imperceptible damage over the years. If you don't know your genetic profile in terms of antioxidant genes and you are physically active, the safest strategy is to eat lots of fruits and vegetables, both good sources of antioxidants.

FIGHTING INFLAMMATION
If you are genetically susceptible to chronic inflammation, it's important to eat anti-inflammatory foods. However, this is particularly crucial if you engage in exercise. Your diet should include sources of anti-inflammatory foods (see text box "Anti-inflammatory food fight," p. 45).

B VITAMIN SUPPLY

Another nutritional choice that becomes particularly important for people who exercise is an adequate supply of the B vitamin folate, also known as folic acid. Earlier in this book (see chapter 3), we discussed how some people with specific genetic variants need to consume more than the currently recommended amounts of folate to lower their levels of homocysteine, a risk factor for heart disease. Studies show that recreational athletes who engage in endurance sport, such as long-distance running, can develop a tendency toward increased levels of homocysteine unless they consume adequate levels of folate and vitamin B12. Therefore, if you are a runner and want to improve your heart health, increase folate in your diet (see text box "B vitamins," p. 34). It's not going to necessarily enhance your performance, but it's certainly an important step for protecting your health.

EXERCISE ADVICE

To your sporting good health, here's a short question-and-answer session with Paula Robson-Ansley, PhD, Senior Lecturer in the Department of Sport and Exercise Sciences, University of Portsmouth, United Kingdom.

▶ **Why exercise?**
Regular endurance exercise of low or moderate intensity can bring a host of health benefits and reduce the risk of premature death from preventable diseases. Exercise can accomplish the following:
- Reduce the risk of coronary heart disease and diabetes.
- Reduce the risk of developing high blood pressure or help lower blood pressure if it is already high.
- Reduce the risk of developing colon cancer and breast cancer.
- Alleviate depression and anxiety and promote psychological well-being.
- Help control body weight.
- Help to build and maintain healthy bones, muscles and joints.

••• *continued* •••

EXERCISE ADVICE *(continued)*

▶ **Can anybody exercise?**

Before embarking on a program that includes vigorous exercise, consult your physician for a medical examination if you belong to one of these categories:

- Men over 40 years of age.
- Women over 50 years of age.
- People at a high risk of heart disease (eg., people with high blood pressure, obesity, diabetes or high cholesterol levels).

If you have any doubts about the state of your health, be sure to consult your physician before beginning your exercise program.

▶ **How much to exercise?**

When deciding to exercise regularly, keep in mind the following 4 basic factors: (1) the type, (2) the frequency, (3) the duration and (4) the intensity of your exercising.

✓ **Type of exercise**

Try to vary the type of exercise. This is important if you want to keep exercising for life and not drop it after a few weeks. The most popular types of exercise are walking, running, hiking, cycling, swimming, dancing and aerobics. If you are not fit enough to jog, start with walking and gradually increase your pace and distance until you reach the recommended level of exercise that is associated with health benefits.

✓ **Frequency of exercise**

Research has shown that, for health benefits, it is optimal to exercise 5 days a week, though more frequent exercise will bring additional benefits. Start with 3 times a week and build it up to 5 times a week or more. The American College of Sports Medicine recommends that people exercise 3 to 5 times each week, but if weight loss is a major goal, they should participate in aerobic activity for at least 30 minutes 5 days each week. All too often, an enthusiastic individual will embark on a daily exercise program only to stop from exhaustion and injury a few weeks later. Try to keep your exercise moderate and remember you are aiming for a lifestyle change rather than following a passing fad.

••• *continued* •••

EXERCISE ADVICE *(continued)*

✓ **Duration of exercise**

According to recent research, the minimum duration of an exercise session is 30 minutes, ideally building it up to 45 minutes to an hour. If you find it hard to fit a single exercise session into a busy day, break it down into multiple shorter sessions totalling at least 30 minutes, which will bring you similar health benefits. The American College of Sports Medicine recommends that you warm up for 5 to 10 minutes before aerobic activity, maintain your exercise intensity for 30 to 45 minutes, then gradually decrease it and stretch to cool down for the last 5 to 10 minutes.

✓ **Intensity of exercise**

Unfortunately, many people are put off by exercise because they believe one needs to work hard to derive any benefit from physical activity. In fact, you do not need to push yourself to exhaustion to gain health benefits from exercise. It is recommended that you work at 50 to 60 percent of your maximal aerobic capacity, which is a fairly low intensity of exercise. As a general guide, make sure you can talk while exercising; if you cannot hold a conversation, this means you are exercising too hard. However, if you choose walking as your preferred type of exercise, make sure it is brisk and not a stroll!

TIPS TO KEEP YOU EXERCISING

Once you decide to start exercising, the following tips from Paula Robson-Ansley, PhD, can help you get started and stick with your exercise program:

▶ **Set achievable goals**
Do not aim for running a marathon if you have done no exercise for the past decade. Modest goals give you a healthy chance of experiencing the thrill of victory, rather than the motivation-busting agony of defeat. Reassess your goals regularly. Tell your friends and family that you have started an exercise program, so they can encourage you to keep exercising if your enthusiasm starts to wane.

▶ **Be realistic**
If you are overweight, start with gentle swimming or walking and gradually build it up. Before long, you will be doing far better than you ever imagined.

▶ **Find an exercise partner**
Apart from helping motivate each other, you can keep each other company while exercising. A dog, always a willing partner, can be great company if you are walking or jogging!

▶ **Invest in appropriate equipment for the type of exercise you choose**
The success of our exercise program does not depend on the amount of money we spend to launch it. However, it is important to buy a good pair of training shoes suitable for the type of exercise you are planning to do, as these will help to prevent injury, which can keep you from exercising. Wear comfortable loose-fitting clothing that is appropriate for the type of exercise you have chosen.

▶ **Try to reward yourself each week if you have attained your exercise goals with a non-food prize**
Such rewards will encourage you to keep exercising.

▶ **Drink while you exercise but don't over drink**
Aim to drink at least 2 liters of fluid per day when not exercising (more if it is very hot) and an additional 10 ounces (300 mL) for every half hour of exercise.

▶ **If you are ill, rest until you have fully recovered**
Do not exercise when you are sick as this can prolong your symptoms and slow down your recovery. Rest until you feel better and, only then, gradually build up your exercise routine.

▶ **And finally**
Enjoy yourself. Some people like team sports. Others like exercising to music. Select activities that you will enjoy rather than simply endure. With so many ways to exercise, you can be creative or try something new in order to pique your interest. Remember, you are far more likely to keep exercising for life if you choose activities that make your life fun!

Chapter 9

· ·

Aging Well

"**A**t seventy you are but a child, at eighty you are merely a youth, and at ninety if the ancestors invite you into heaven, ask them to wait until you are one hundred ... and then you might consider it."

The proverb above from Okinawa – a group of Japanese islands famous, among other things, for its residents' unusual longevity – aptly express- es the universal human desire to live a long life and to hold onto the bloom of youth well into an advanced age. This ancient quest for im- mortality is currently poised for a major marketing push in the Western world – after all, America's baby boomers are already pushing 60!

Baby boomers have reason to be jealous of the Okinawans; unlike their Western counterparts, the elderly population of Okinawa is blessed with a slow, relatively healthy aging process. Searching for the secret behind this and other "successful" aging patterns, scientists have traditionally looked for clues in diet and lifestyle. However, with the advent of the genetic revolution, more and more scientific studies are focusing on the search for genetic clues. Is the rate at which we grow old – and the number of years we ultimately live – determined by our genes?

Although science is still puzzling over the relationship between our genes and aging, it is clear that human lifespan has generally increased over the past 100 years. We owe our longer lives to the successful battle against disease, won through measures that include water purification, antibiotics and vaccines. Such methods have not transported us into some legendary Shangri-la of happy immortals, but advances in medicine and public health have granted millions of people the gift of many additional, disease-free years.

Today, nutritional genomics is poised to conquer the next frontier in healthy aging – maximizing every individual's gene-based potential for a long, healthy life. In this chapter, we'll describe some of the latest advances in the genetics of aging, with an emphasis on research that is already generating practical advice for living longer, and better.

Why do we age?

For geneticists, the puzzle of "why we age" is not a philosophical exercise but a concrete, straightforward question. What are the genetic mechanisms that cause us to gradually lose our youthful appearance and to experience other changes linked with advancing age? And what perverse quirk of evolution set us apart from perpetually young-looking species such as sponges, lobsters and certain fish and turtles?

Many of us have heard of the "biological clock" that ticks away, marking the limited time in which most young people can hope to have children. It turns out that human cells grown in the laboratory have their own kind of "clock," defined by the limited number of times

– usually around 50 – that a cell can divide before it dies. Proposed in 1965 by Leonard Hayflick, PhD, today a professor of anatomy at the University of California, San Francisco, the "clock theory" may provide a partial answer to the riddle of why cells age. Another theory that must be taken into account when considering the lifespan of a cell is that of "random damage" – in which our body's cells sustain random assaults from the environment until accumulated damage finally does them in. In fact, both mechanisms – random damage and a slow "winding down" of the cellular clock – are believed to play a role in aging.

Our understanding of the cellular clock has been enhanced by the study of telomeres, DNA "buffers" found at the end of chromosomes. Researchers discovered that every time a cell divides, the tail end of the DNA fails to get copied. Despite this, thanks to the presence of the telomere buffer – which is clipped, getting slightly shorter with every cell division – no valuable genetic data are lost. When the telomeres get too short, the cell can no longer divide and becomes inactive or dies.

This "self-sacrificing" activity of telomeres goes on throughout our lives. In human white blood cells, for example, the length of telomeres drops from about 8,000 DNA "letters" at birth to 1,500 in the elderly. So can our steadily shrinking telomeres help us gauge the expected lifespan of our cells, like the sands disappearing from the upper half of an hourglass? In a limited sense, the answer might be yes – researchers from the University of Utah have found that shorter telomeres may indeed be associated with shorter lives.

In a study of subjects over the age of 60, people with shorter telomeres were shown to be 3 times more likely to die from heart disease and 8 times more likely to die from infectious disease than people with longer telomeres. However, the telomere-age connection is a sort of chicken-and-egg conundrum; it is not yet clear whether shorter telomeres are a cause or an effect of age-related processes. Moreover, no one knows whether our lives might be extended by preserving, or by somehow restoring, the lopped-off length of our telomeres. And lastly, a word of caution is in order: because it is known that cancer cells activate an enzyme that prevents the shortening of telomeres (not surprisingly, called "telomerase"), it is conceivable that "telomere tampering" might potentially jump-start cancerous growth.

Whatever the true role of telomeres in aging, it's obvious that they are only part of the story. Think of aging as the cumulative deterioration of the body's quality control system – a little mistake here, a little slow-down there – until several decades down the line our cells and tissues can no longer effectively meet the challenges of day-to-day living.

Ultimately, no matter what our chronological age, our genes are never as young as they used to be. As we get older, our genes begin to switch on and off at different rates, producing protective proteins in insufficient amounts and generating inappropriate inflammatory substances. Although there is still much to be discovered about this process, scientists are hard at work, seeking to understand gene-linked aging mechanisms in order to slow down their adverse effects in humans. Among the most important experiments in this area are those that examine the aging process in laboratory animals.

Low calories, long life

Can diet make us live longer? One diet-based anti-aging technique has already granted unusually long life to yeast, worms, spiders, mice and rats. But if you want to know why this technique has not been eagerly adopted by humans, you need look no further than its name: calorie restriction.

Back in the 1930s, researchers demonstrated that a low-calorie diet could actually delay the aging process in laboratory animals. Calorie restriction was also shown to prevent many of the changes in gene function normally associated with aging, including the accumulation of body fat, low heat tolerance and poor insulin metabolism. Subsequently, other scientists managed to quantify this "long-life" factor, demonstrating that mice and rats that consume 25 to 60 percent fewer calories than a normal diet extend their lifetimes by up to 50 percent. Translated into human terms – assuming human subjects would respond similarly under the same conditions – clamping down on our calorie count could mean extending our lives by about 40 years! No less exciting is the fact that the mice and rats fed a restricted diet continue to look and act young much longer than the well-fed control animals. They are also much less likely to develop cancer, diabetes and a host of other diseases.

No one knows whether people can really achieve longer and healthier lives by drastically cutting down on calories. Documented examples in which population groups suffer from calorie restriction are generally complicated by the nature of the food consumed; when calorie intake is low, the foods people do manage to eat are often of poor quality and lack vital nutrients. Not only does this low-calorie diet fail to add years to human life, it actually leads to poor health by contributing to short stature, fertility problems and a host of other medical complications.

On the other hand, studies that have highlighted the effect of low-calorie, high-quality nutrition on life expectancy have produced fascinating – if inconclusive – results. For example, the Okinawans described earlier in this chapter, consume 20 percent less calories than the Japanese average. They also have about 40 percent fewer deaths from stroke, cancer and heart disease than in the rest of Japan. Although there are probably other lifestyle, environmental and genetic differences between the populations in Okinawa and mainland Japan, the startling difference between Okinawans and their more well-fed neighbors is definitely food for thought.

One of the reasons that scientists have thus far been unable to reach a definitive conclusion about the link between aging and calorie restriction is the time factor. Imagine how long a calorie restriction study would have to last to establish whether human life span could be extended, say, from 80 to 90 years. And even if the semi-starvation diet were found to be beneficial in humans, it's hard to imagine that many people would jump at the opportunity to participate in such a trial!

Radical damage

Given the improbability of large-scale human population studies related to calorie restriction and aging, scientists around the world are attacking this question from the bottom up, by examining the effect of calorie restriction on molecular processes. According to the latest research, it seems that one of the most beneficial side effects of cutting calorie intake might be the slowing down of the silent, yet harmful condition called oxidative stress.

Believed to be a major cause of aging, oxidative stress comes from the very air we breathe. As our cells process oxygen from the air, they convert a small fraction of the incoming oxygen molecules into unruly, negatively charged by-products called free radicals. As discussed in chapter 4, these molecular "delinquents" are highly destructive – grabbing electrons from neighboring molecules to make up a pair. In so doing, they set off a chain reaction that inflicts severe damage upon DNA, proteins and fats, and can trigger a host of diseases. In addition to normal oxygen metabolism, free radicals can be produced in response to environmental factors, such as ultraviolet light, chemotherapy or environmental toxins.

The theory that aging is largely the result of the havoc wreaked by oxidative stress was first proposed back in the 1950s. Initially quite controversial, during the past decade or so this idea has gradually received support from the research community. This support increased when oxidative stress was shown to have a genetic component.

The DNA of aging cells in a variety of species, including humans, appears badly "bruised" by the insults inflicted over time by free radicals.

To study the consequences of these insults, researchers have developed a number of "model systems" – different organisms that carry out many of the same cellular activities as human beings but, unlike humans, are readily manipulated in the laboratory. Using model systems such as worms and fruit flies, it's been possible to explore the genetic link between aging and oxidative stress.

The results have been compelling. Both worms and fruit flies with genetic variants that enhance resistance to oxidative stress live much longer than their counterparts with the more common, regular versions of these genes. For example, worms with a certain protective gene variant that confers greater resistance to ultraviolet radiation and heat – as well as other stress factors known to generate free radicals – live twice as long as worms without the protective variant. Moreover, scientists have used genetic technologies to prolong the lives of worms and flies by causing them to synthesize increased amounts of antioxidants – protective substances that neutralize oxidative stress.

If oxidative stress is indeed a leading factor in aging, then nutritional genomics stands an excellent chance of forestalling adverse, age-linked effects. By increasing our intake of antioxidant-rich foods, we can bolster our body's natural line of defense against free radicals. Moreover, by lowering levels of oxidative stress, we may reduce the risk of many diseases associated with aging.

A word of caution, however: antioxidants have yet to prove themselves as an elixir of youth. In studies with laboratory mammals, for example, antioxidant dietary supplements have had little or no effect on longevity. Still, it is possible that an effective anti-aging strategy based on antioxidants may yet be formulated once we have more information – we must learn more about how antioxidants work, how they are absorbed by tissues, how they are metabolized in the body, which antioxidants can best compensate for which genetic faults and which intake levels are required to get the desired effect.

It's Not Just Your Genes!

In the future, recommendations for the optimal type and amount of antioxidants will be made based on each person's gene variants, leading to personalized nutritional strategies for averting the harmful effects of oxidative stress. In the meantime, your best bet is to eat plenty of antioxidants, particularly if your antioxidant genes are not functioning at an optimal level (see chapter 4). In addition, we advise you to minimize your exposure to environmental stress factors that are liable to raise your levels of free radicals and produce other undesirable effects in your body (see text box "Putting a stop to the 'stress'," below).

PUTTING A STOP TO THE "STRESS"

Our bodies are regularly assaulted by a variety of stress factors – harmful influences that can take a significant cumulative toll, especially if the protective systems encoded in our genes are less than robust. These stress factors function on a molecular or cellular level and include free radicals, infectious organisms, heat and cold, ultraviolet radiation – to name just a few. Throughout this book we have addressed nutritional and lifestyle strategies for reducing the damaging impact of such stress factors, but simply avoiding or at least minimizing exposure can also help improve the quality – and perhaps even the duration – of our lives. Here are a few tips for putting a stop to the stress:

▸ **Smoking**
  If you smoke, make every effort to quit. Smoking is always harmful, but the harm increases with age, as our body's toxin-removing systems slow down.

▸ **Temperature extremes**
  Avoid exposure to temperature extremes – both heat and cold are cellular stressors.

▸ **Ultraviolet radiation**
  To limit exposure to UV radiation, stay out of the sun between 11 am and 2 pm – when the solar rays are particularly strong – and use protective sunscreen.

••• *continued* •••

PUTTING A STOP TO THE "STRESS" *(continued)*

▸ **Food**
Avoid going to extremes in the amount of food you eat: both starvation and over-feeding are stressful to the body.

▸ **Toxins in your food**
Avoid toxic chemicals in food. Among the more common toxins that contaminate our food supply are antibiotics and hormones given to farm animals, heavy metals that accumulate in fish and herbicides and pesticides used to increase the yield of plant crops. One solution is to purchase organic animal and plant products when you can.

▸ **Toxins in the home**
Rid your home and office of toxic cleaning supplies, which contain volatile organic molecules that get into the air and can land in your lungs or on your skin. Choose environmentally friendly products from manufacturers who are committed to avoiding the use of toxic chemicals.

▸ **Sleep**
Get adequate sleep on a daily basis. "Running on empty" all week and trying to make up for it on the weekend is a recipe for stress.

▸ **Infection**
Minimize exposure to infections of any kind, from infectious diseases to potential contamination in foods. Always wash your hands before eating or cooking, and keep cold foods cold (40° F or below) and hot foods hot (above 140° F). Thaw frozen food in the refrigerator rather than at room temperature, and never allow cooked food to stand at room temperature for more than 2 hours.

Clearly aging is still an intriguing mystery - and a complex one at that - but it's also the focus of numerous research teams dedicated to providing answers as to why and how we age and what it means to age well. From what we already know, there are a number of steps we can take now to lay a healthy foundation for our later years. As nutritional genomics research progresses and the research is translated into practical dietary and lifestyle changes we can make, we can look forward to more years in our life and more life in our years.

The inflammation theory of aging

Oxidative stress is not the only process associated with aging. In fact, it is believed to act in concert with yet another prime suspect – inflammation, which can be triggered by an over-supply of free radicals.

But let's back up for a moment to calorie restriction. The theory that chronic inflammation is a major player in aging is supported by studies of animals fed a low-calorie diet. In addition to decreasing oxidative stress, such calorie restriction also appears to reduce inflammation – it blunts the action of genes involved in the inflammation process and suppresses the production of inflammatory substances in experimental animals.

Such research suggests that inflammation has an exceedingly long "rap-sheet" – in addition to being involved in heart disease, diabetes, osteoporosis and obesity, chronic inflammation contributes to aging itself. If you still need convincing, this is yet another reason to include anti-inflammatory foods in your diet, particularly if your genes put you at an increased risk of chronic inflammation (see text box "Anti-inflammatory food fight," p. 45).

Aging DNA

In addition to fighting oxidative stress and inflammation by eating the right foods, a key to healthy aging is staying fit. But fitness is not just about our bodies, it is also important to the integrity – and the smooth functioning – of our DNA.

It appears that, as we grow older, the condition of our DNA gradually declines. We are not talking about alterations that might occasionally occur in its genetic "letters" but rather about the deterioration of the DNA molecule itself. DNA undergoes changes that are "epigenetic" (from the Greek prefix epi, meaning, among other things, "upon" or "above"). Such changes modify the chemical composition and functioning of DNA without affecting the genetic code. The relatively new branch of science that studies these modifications is called epigenetics.

Among the many issues it addresses, epigenetics asks a basic and very important question: what turns genes on and off? We already know part of the answer: DNA is outfitted with molecular "tags" known as methyl groups, which serve as on/off switches for individual genes. When these tags are in place, they keep the gene silent; when the tag is removed, the gene starts the biochemical process that will result in the production of a protein.

The entire drama of life, from the dawn of fetal development to the sunset of old age, is governed by this on/off system. In the developing fetus and throughout our lifetimes, on/off switches determine the fate of each cell. Whether a cell will become a heart, muscle or brain cell depends on the genes that are activated in its nucleus. When this switching mechanism is disrupted, the result is chaos. Faulty "switching" can lead to disease.

In aging, and in the case of certain diseases, it seems that the DNA molecule gets "out of shape," losing its optimal chemical composition, and in turn, disrupting the system of genetic switches. Methyl-group tags that control the way the genes work wander off track, attaching to DNA molecules in the wrong places. In cancer, for example, misplaced methyl groups apparently switch on tumor-promoting genes and silence tumor-suppressing genes. Faulty methyl-group tagging is also believed to contribute to Alzheimer's and Parkinson's diseases.

Although there is no way to guarantee that you will avoid disease altogether, the incidence of certain conditions linked to faulty DNA tagging can be influenced by proper nutrition. The formation of DNA tags is dependent on the food we eat, and eating a diet that provides an adequate supply of the building blocks for making these tags is an essential factor for DNA "fitness." And in terms of eating right for DNA health, it's never too early; studies suggest that inadequate nutrition in the womb or shortly after birth can increase the risk of chronic conditions in adulthood such as heart disease, diabetes and cancer. Moreover, animal studies show that the DNA tends to "remember" certain aspects of its chemical composition that were determined during early development – it's quite possible that this composition, in turn, affects our susceptibility to disease throughout our lives.

So what should be on the menu if we want to promote tip-top DNA function up to and including our later years? One of the most important nutrients for DNA integrity is the B vitamin folate, also known as folic acid. Folate is a critical component in the formation of the methyl groups that form the DNA tags. Additionally, an inadequate folate supply can quite literally shatter our genetic material; in 2004, California researchers showed that folate deficiency can subject the DNA to breakage similar to that caused by exposure to significant levels of radiation. Apparently, insufficient folate levels can lead not only to "malfunctions" in the genetic switches but also to a structural weakening of the entire DNA molecule.

The United States food industry practices folate fortification, making sure that it is easy to get an adequate supply of folate through grains and cereals, in addition to the green leafy vegetables in which folate is naturally found. However, many people still fail to consume sufficient amounts of folate, which is particularly risky for individuals with gene variants that impair folate metabolism (for more about folate deficiency and its relation to heart disease, see chapter 3).

Though the precise role of DNA "fitness" in aging is still unclear, if we want our body cells to function properly over the long term, strong and healthy DNA – containing few breaks and with all its chemical tags in the right places – is obviously a significant advantage. We strongly recommend that you do not wait for all the pieces of this scientific puzzle to be fit together. Rather, starting today, your healthy aging plan of action should include measures aimed at using the knowledge currently available to keep your DNA fit.

Gene-smart recommendations for healthy aging

Like any piece of machinery that has seen better days, the aging human body may be prone to breakdowns. However, we have one tremendous advantage over machines: in the human body a team of "molecular mechanics" is continuously on patrol, warding off or even repairing damage. Our bodies are defended by naturally occurring systems that fight oxidative stress, remove harmful toxins and repair DNA damage. While aging itself is unavoidable, at least at our current level of knowledge, it is possible to adopt strategies – matched to our individual genetic profile – that will boost our bodies' natural defenses. Here are some general suggestions for aging well:

REDUCE OXIDATIVE STRESS

To reduce the harmful condition known as oxidative stress, eat plenty of foods rich in antioxidants (see text box "Antioxidant-rich foods," p. 63). Recent research suggests that antioxidants can even delay age-related disorders of the brain and nervous system, such as Alzheimer's disease.

Fruits and vegetables are the key components of an antioxidant-rich diet. It's hard to overestimate the value of these foods – they are believed to lower the risk of many chronic diseases, and their protective features become all the more crucial as we age and as years of oxidative stress begin to take a toll on our body's tissues.

This advice holds for everybody, but it is especially relevant for you if your genes fall short of providing you with optimal protection against oxidative stress (see chapter 4), a deficiency that tends to become more severe as we get older.

KEEP INFLAMMATION IN CHECK

Chronic inflammation is thought to promote aging, including – that bane of our elderly existence! – the aging of the skin. As a result of recent research, inflammatory substances are now implicated in many age-related conditions including heart disease, type 2 diabetes and certain neurological disorders (see chapters 3 and 5). Moreover, as we age, our genes are more likely to produce inflammatory substances at inappropriate times or in inappropriate amounts. If your genes put you at an increased risk of chronic inflammation, you should make sure to consume anti-inflammatory foods on a regular basis (see text box "Anti-inflammatory food fight," p. 45).

HELP YOUR BODY CLEANSE ITSELF

Our bodies have a set of natural cleansing mechanisms, called detoxifiers, which remove harmful substances that enter our bodies from the air we breathe and the food we eat. However, in people with certain genetic profiles, these mechanisms do not perform well, and in general, the genes responsible for detoxification tend to slow down with age. Therefore, older people should be particularly careful to boost the function of their detoxification genes with adequate nutritional support. For more on detoxification and the foods that promote it, see chapter 4. In addition, you can do your part to keep your body clean – inside and out – by avoiding smoking and toxin-loaded foods (see text box "Putting a stop to the 'stress'," p. 144).

HELP YOUR DNA STAY "FIT"

As discussed earlier in this chapter, DNA tends to deteriorate with age, causing a disruption of vital cellular processes. Healthy nutrition, particularly an adequate supply of folate and other B vitamins (see text box "B vitamins," p. 34), can help prevent excessive DNA damage.

STRENGTHEN YOUR BONES

Like all other body systems, our bones need adequate nutrition in order to stay healthy and strong, particularly as we advance in years.

The amount of calcium and other bone-building nutrients you consume should ideally be adjusted to your genetic profile (see chapter 6). Also crucial for bone health is weight-bearing exercise, which not only builds up a hardy, resilient skeleton but also promotes strong muscles (see "Weight-bearing exercise," p. 98). Both nutrition and exercise are important for maintaining your bone health – and ensuring your independence – well into an advanced age.

MAINTAIN A HEALTHY WEIGHT

As we age, our metabolism slows down and we are more prone to accumulating body fat. Therefore, avoiding junk food and extra calories becomes significantly more important as we get older. Among its many benefits, exercise can also help you keep a healthy weight throughout your lifetime (see chapter 7 for more about genes and weight).

EXERCISE

Physical activity improves our health and well-being at every stage in our lives, but it becomes vitally important as we approach our golden years. In addition to helping keep the body strong and flexible and reducing the risk of many age-related diseases, it also helps prevent falls and fractures, major causes of disability among the elderly. Moreover, physical activity elevates the spirits and creates opportunities for social interaction, which can be particularly helpful for people who are no longer part of the workforce.

The types of exercise you choose can be adjusted as you age – many older people opt for low-impact activities including walking, swimming, stretching, dancing, gardening, hiking and cycling. Yoga is good for toning the body and mind, and the "soft" martial art tai-chi, which can be taken up at any age, is an excellent way to improve both self-confidence and balance (see boxes "Exercise advice" p. 132 and "Tips to keep you exercising," p. 135).

Chapter 10

Who Has the Right to Know?
Privacy in Genetic Testing

By David Castle, PhD
Associate Professor
Department of Philosophy
University of Guelph
Ontario, Canada

Nutritional genomics is about knowledge. Modern scientific techniques are expanding the definition of what is knowable by making it possible to reveal detailed information about what makes a person tick – biologically speaking. Because it relates to a specific individual, such information, like any medical test results, is something you may wish to keep private. But since it is gathered through genetic testing performed by others, on some level this information will always have to be shared between you and someone else.

The very nature of genetic testing, therefore, raises an important question: how can you keep your personal information private, and under what circumstances should it be made public? You might wish to keep this information completely to yourself. If someone must know – for

153

example, if you decide to share the screening results with your doctor – you might want to ensure that this information is not passed on to others.

Like anyone who prefers not to share information about his or her medical history or credit rating, you have the right to demand that the information disclosed in your genetic screening remain private. First of all, let's state the obvious: the results of your testing are personal, so in this sense they are truly no one else's business. Second, such results might point toward general susceptibilities or tendencies – rather than providing any clear-cut, medical diagnosis – and are therefore open to erroneous interpretation. You might have concerns about how your employer or insurance company would interpret your results, for example.

This being said, concerns about employer and insurer access to genetic information are sometimes overstated. Despite a steady growth in the use of genetic testing, there have been just a handful of legal cases in which genetic information was said to have been used to discriminate against individuals. Also, many countries are well aware of the potential privacy issues involved and have instituted safeguards. For example, the 1990 Americans with Disabilities Act has been extended to protect people from discrimination based on their genetic profile. The US Senate has also passed a genetic nondiscrimination bill, and the United Kingdom has a moratorium in place that restricts the use of genetic information by insurers and employers.

Privacy is also a priority for the academic community. As the Human Genome Project progressed, bioethicists have vigorously debated the issue of public access to private genetic information and continue to do so. This ongoing conversation about privacy has influenced law and policy makers. As a result, the most serious kinds of potential abuse are already on society's watch-list.

154

All this is not to downplay the importance of genetic privacy. As the genetic age unfolds, however, it turns out that many of the most serious concerns are usually subtler than the possibility of outright genetic discrimination.

Think about it: genetics is a family affair, and the benefits you reap from nutritional genomics may, in some cases, have an impact on your relatives. Despite your decision to undergo genetic screening, your parents, siblings or your children might not want to know what you know – particularly if it involves a susceptibility to a frightening-sounding medical condition. Under such circumstances, keeping your information private becomes a serious, personal responsibility. Not only will you have to carefully consider whether you tell your family what you have learned about yourself, you may also have to decide about having your children tested, with all the ramifications such a decision might hold for the future.

When you deliver your genetic information into someone else's hands, you should have control over how they will handle it. You have the right to demand assurances that this information will be kept private. A signed confidentiality agreement should state what will happen to your information and ensure that it cannot be passed on to other people such as family members or potential employers. In addition, whomever you trust with your information should be able to provide clear answers about how this it is to be kept secure. Privacy, confidentiality and security – you'll want to remember these terms. Together, they will help you to be proactive about protecting your genetic information.

Sometimes concerns are raised about the difference between privacy standards implemented in private companies as opposed to public research institutions. The presumption is that profit motive induces lax standards for privacy, whereas public institutions can be trusted to be the "guardian angels" of your genetic information. Definitive proof for either claim is not available, and unfortunately, both good and bad examples can be lined up on either side of the debate. Therefore, it is important to familiarize yourself with the privacy protocols governing any institution with which you choose to share your screening results and, as stated above, stand up for your right to privacy, confidentiality and security.

Privacy issues are also raised by the relative ease with which genetic samples are gathered. Whether you go to a doctor or genetic counselor for screening or employ the services of a gene-analysis company, the procedure is usually so simple it doesn't even require a blood test. Just swab the inside of your mouth, hand over your sample, and your DNA will be extracted. The question is: what happens to the sample after the results are in?

You might ask, "Why worry about what they do with my sample? After all, during the course of a day we shed skin cells and hair all over the place and no one thinks of it as a security issue!"

It is true that each cell of the body, with the exception of red blood cells, contains exactly the same DNA, so that in principle a full genetic analysis can be "extracted" from any part of your anatomy (see appendix "Genetic testing – how does it work?"). It's exceedingly difficult, however, and sometimes impossible to perform DNA testing when the cells are few in number, as is usually the case with randomly gathered bits of skin and hair. When you give a sample to your doctor or to a company, on the other hand, you've provided them with a "letter" that is designed to be opened and read. Like any confidential "correspondence," it should not be left lying around.

Again, you have the right to be proactive. Ask your medical practitioner or gene analysis company what will happen to your sample once your genetic information is extracted. Will it be destroyed? If so, when and how will this happen? Will it be kept for future use by the company? Will it be donated or sold to another private firm or public research institution so that more information can be collected from it? Answers to questions such as these – even if you receive a satisfactory response face-to-face – should be included in any confidentiality agreement that you sign.

Be aware that sharing your genetic information with a company or a public health authority – while observing all the safeguards described above – might ultimately bring you additional benefits beyond knowing your individual susceptibility to disease. Professionally gathered genetic information can contribute greatly to public health, by helping researchers or private companies develop new products and services. Such secondary use of your genetic information is not illegal, and it is not a violation of your privacy – so long as you agree to it. You should, however, know what you are agreeing to.

Secondary use of genetic information brings up additional, complex privacy issues. For example, you might agree to have your genetic information used in research studies, but you may not want to have this information linked to identifying parameters such as your name, address, sex, age, weight or ethnicity. One solution would be to ask that your genetic information, if it is used, remain completely anonymous. There is a catch, however: what if subsequent research reveals new and useful knowledge about how your diet, lifestyle and genes interact? If you want to take advantage of such late-breaking developments, you might want to consider trading your anonymity for the right to be contacted with health-promoting advice by researchers.

Finally, we should say a word about the changing culture of genetic testing. Until recently, genetic screening was used only to search for genes causing disorders with severe consequences. People wishing to know their own risk of developing a life-threatening disorder such as Huntington's disease would undergo testing, as would couples wishing to avoid the possibility of passing on genetic disorders to their children.

The genetic testing referred to in this book provides information about susceptibility to disease. Such tests cannot diagnose the presence or absence of a disease now, nor can they predict the future incidence of disease with any certainty. Sometimes these genes are called "lifestyle" genes in order to emphasize that their negative effects will only come into play if they are combined with poor lifestyle choices.

In terms of privacy concerns, however, there is no difference between "lifestyle" genetic testing and tests that hunt for genes linked to hereditary disease. In many countries, the standard for approving a test for nutritional genomics is as high as any other genetic test administered in a medical context, which is how it ought to be. There is an important difference between the impact such tests can have: whereas screening for a disease may reveal serious and unavoidable health issues in your immediate future, screening for "lifestyle" genes can empower you by providing options for diet and lifestyle choice that can change your future for the better.

Here are a few suggestions and issues to consider when you undergo genetic testing:

▸ Ask about the kind of genes that will be screened and the kind of information you will derive from the test.

▸ Undergoing genetic testing is a personal decision, and you have the right to define the parameters of the screening process. Ask yourself: is there anything about the test or uses of your DNA sample to which you did not agree? If so, the testing procedure can – and should – be changed.

▸ Ask about the privacy policy of the company or research institution that is performing your genetic test. Privacy should cover both your physical DNA sample and the information it contains. Do you know for sure what will happen to your sample and to your genetic information?

▶ Remember, proper handling of your screening is based on three things: The *privacy* of your information, a *confidentiality* agreement, and the *security* measures used to protect both your results and your DNA sample.

▶ When you get your results, keep them private if you wish. In any event, any written reports should be kept in a secure location.

Genetic testing for "lifestyle" genes has created a new world of possibilities for personalized health promotion. By understanding the privacy issues, and taking a few simple steps, you can confidently add to your knowledge while ensuring that your personal information remains fully under your control.

Chapter 11

. . . .

The Gene-smart Shopping Experience: Your Health Is "In the Bag"

Remember Paul and Jennifer? After getting personalized advice from a nutritional genomics practitioner, they've gotten serious about eating right. Today, it's Jennifer's turn to do the shopping in the Supermarket of the Future, and she's packing her purse with everything she needs: her wallet, her keys and the two special gene cards that – thanks to their local supermarket's computerized Gene-smart Shopping interface – will help guide her quickly to the food products with the greatest health benefits for both her and her husband.

After grabbing a cart, Jennifer heads straight for the service desk, where a touch-screen console lays out her shopping choices. Pleased to see that this store offers fully automated menu planning in addition to the standard "Gene-ius" product-selection software, she chooses breakfast, lunch and

dinner for a 3-day period. Asked for the number of people who will be eat-
ing, she chooses two, and then slips the gene cards into the slot, one after the
other, and types in a special security code. She is momentarily startled by
the question that appears on the screen.

"Are you pregnant?" she reads, marveling at the program's level of detail.
Then, with a quick glance around to make sure no one is looking, she gives
her answer. "Maybe in a few more months," she thinks with a smile.

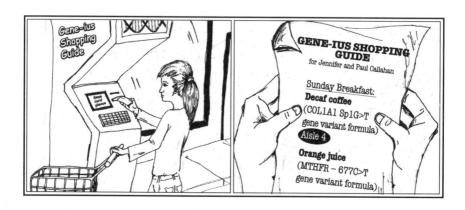

Jennifer scans the menu plan with its integrated shopping list and breathes
a grateful sigh. This sure takes the headache out of trying to remember
– and balance – all the various bits of advice she and Paul received from
the nutritional genomics practitioner. For instance, she can't quite recall the
name of the gene that gives her a tendency toward increased inflammatory
response, but no matter: it's right there in the report. And all the omega-3
fatty acids her body needs to counteract this problem will be staring her
right in the face – over at the fish counter!

Next, Jennifer heads to the produce section. Nutritional genomics counsel-
ing has made her aware just how important fruits and vegetables are for
her body, because of gene variants that make it difficult to neutralize toxins
– a serious problem for someone like her, who only recently quit smoking.

Fresh produce is also important for Paul; when there's a ready supply of fruit in the house, he's much less likely to turn to fatty snacks, which are bad for his cholesterol. Also, since he has the APOE4 gene variant, Paul's cholesterol levels might soar if he doesn't watch his saturated fats.

While stocking up on a wide variety of nutrient-rich produce, her shopping list reminds her that highly-colored fruits and vegetables are rich in beta-carotene, which is a good source of antioxidants – a worthy diet investment given her family's cancer history. The list also directs her to a brand-new product line that matches her genetic profile: hot-house broccoli bred to be especially rich in folic acid, vitamin C and glucosinolates – a natural compound found in broccoli, cauliflower and cabbage that helps boost the enzymes in her body's relatively weak detoxification system. She makes another checkmark on her computer print-out. "Cream of Gene vegetable soup," she thinks. "Great idea!"

Now it's time to pick up that bone-strengthening "Fit'n Your Genes" sports drink for Paul, as well as some orange juice – an important item on their leisurely Sunday breakfast menu. Jennifer marvels at all the specially labeled cartons – personalized, gene-based nutrition has sure changed the OJ market, she thinks, and in a big way!

It's Not Just Your Genes!

Jennifer's favored OJ packs a lot more than just vitamin C – although, of course, it has that, too. The "added value" of this juice is in its fortified dose of B vitamins, which not only helps reduce her risk of heart disease, but also serves to protect her DNA from age-related deterioration. This is important for Jennifer, whose genetic profile – which includes the 677C>T variant of the MTHFR gene – puts her at risk for these conditions if her B vitamin intake doesn't match up to her gene-based requirement. She especially likes this brand because it includes some added calcium for bone health and also plant sterols, which are indicated for Paul with his high cholesterol.

As she places the juice in her shopping cart, Jennifer recalls that her nutritional counselor emphasized how important it was for her to eat adequate amounts of the B vitamin known as folate, especially if she was considering getting pregnant. Jennifer double checks her shopping cart to make sure she picked up some folate-rich spinach back in the produce department. Then, after balancing her fortified orange juice on top of the lettuce, she heads to the checkout line.

The gene-smart shopping experience described above is still a dream. But as more and more people wake up to the real-world benefits of genetic screening, incorporating science-based considerations into our nutrition and lifestyle choices is destined to become as natural as a trip to the store.

In fact, while commercial food products are not yet available according to potential customers' personal genetic profiles, scientific advances are already beginning to have a profound impact on the way we eat, in the form of new – and very popular – "functional foods."

Take yogurt, for example. Always a healthy choice, today's yogurt comes in a variety of high-tech formulations, including yogurts with added "probiotics" – bacteria that follow the yogurt down into our gut and stay there to promote better digestion. Eggs – the boogey man of our collective heart-health nightmares – are now available with increased levels of omega-3 fatty acids and lowered cholesterol. Smoothies are fortified with antioxidants. Even ketchup – the most familiar condiment – is available with added lycopene, a natural substance found in tomatoes and red-colored fruits such as watermelon and pink grapefruit, which may help prevent prostate cancer. Apparently, where scientific research goes, our grocery list follows close behind.

As more people turn to nutritional genomic screening as the basis for a personalized plan for diet and lifestyle, this will trigger an increased demand for food products tailored to meet specific, gene-based requirements. No longer content with wandering the aisles searching aimlessly for foods rich in B vitamins or high in calcium, consumers will look to food manufacturers and retailers to help them identify foods that can best fulfill their specific requirements.

How are you going to recognize these foods when you go to the supermarket of the future? Unlike the futuristic shopping scenario described above, it's unlikely that manufacturers will be allowed to declare that one food or another affects a particular gene anytime soon. Given the present state of our knowledge, it is still too early, in most cases, to state such things with precision. However, product labels can highlight beneficial components, and, armed with data gleaned from genetic screening, it is already possible for individual consumers to find the food products most appropriate for their needs.

Beyond what you can get in the grocery store, nutritional genomics is also paving the way for "custom" dietary supplements formulated to match a specific genetic profile. Such supplements can fill in the gap in cases where an individual is unable to meet his or her nutritional needs through diet alone.

All these developments – customized nutrition, more functional foods and tailor-made dietary supplements – mark the beginning of a welcome trend toward personalized, preventive health. Nutritional genomics creates a whole new kind of health strategy, in which gene-based vulnerabilities are detected early, before they have had a chance to have a harmful effect on your body. Together with changes in lifestyle, gene-smart nutrition empowers you to pursue proactive steps toward a fuller and healthier life.

With this power comes responsibility. The new science of nutritional genomics will see consumers taking control of their own health destiny and making informed decisions that can help prevent disease over the long term. Moreover, by adopting a diet and lifestyle regimen that is in tune with their genetic profiles, consumers will feel better on a daily basis, by conscientiously incorporating science-based health management into their lives.

There's a huge difference between "following a diet" and knowing what's good for you and why. As a knowledge-based discipline, nutritional genomics increases your motivation to preserve your health, by making it clear where you should be directing your energies. In other words, you are in charge of your future, at the maximum level that science allows you to be. That's what empowerment is all about.

We hope that the knowledge contained in this book has left you with a sense of empowerment. Today, we understand that what you need to know is there for the asking, right in your genes. Go forth and learn – and you'll find out how good you can feel – today, tomorrow, and for the rest of your life.

. . . .

Appendix

....

Genetic Testing:
How Does It Work?

In this book, we've discussed the way genetic testing can help you develop a personal, gene-based strategy for healthy living. But how is this testing actually performed? Here's a step-by-step, "behind the scenes" tour of DNA analysis:

Step 1 – Collecting the sample

Genetic testing is a sophisticated, high-tech procedure, but the first step – collection of the DNA sample – is strikingly simple. In fact, genetic testing performed to generate dietary and lifestyle advice doesn't even require a blood test. To collect a DNA sample, you just rub the inside of your cheek with a sterile swab. The swab is then sent to the company or institution that will perform the analysis.

The rubbing gathers just enough cells from your cheek lining to complete the testing. That's because the cells of your cheek, like all other cells of your body with the exception of red blood cells, contain exactly the same DNA. This is why you may have heard about DNA being extracted from a variety of tissues for use in criminal forensics; no matter where the cells come from – blood, semen, or hair – they contain all the genes that make you who you are.

Step 2 – Genetic copying machine

After the right DNA has been separated out, there's still a problem: based on your limited cell sample, there's not enough DNA to run all the genetic tests. This problem is solved with the help of polymerase chain reaction (PCR), a genetic technology invented in the 1980s. Roughly the equivalent of a DNA copying machine for DNA, PCR has revolutionized molecular biology and won its inventor the Nobel Prize in Chemistry in 1993. In a matter of hours, PCR can multiply the original DNA sample a million times, producing enough DNA for analysis.

Step 3 – Unzipping the zipper

We can now focus on the genes or parts of genes that are of interest to us. But how do we identify the relevant DNA segments? These segments are "fished out" using molecular "baits" that have been designed to match target DNA segments.

First, scientists separate, or "unzip", the two strands previously coiled together in DNA's famous double-helix structure. Once the two strands of this corkscrew-shaped ladder have been unzipped, the unoccupied "rungs" become available – chemically speaking – and "eager" to hook up and form another bond. That's where the "bait" – the molecular probe – enters the picture.

Molecular probes for genetic screening are engineered to match a very specific target segment of "unzipped" genetic material. When such a probe finds its match, the unzipped DNA segment "zips up" again into a double-helix shape. And because of special, fluorescent molecules embedded in the probe, this "zipping" causes the DNA/probe complex to light up, notifying scientists that a particular gene segment has been found.

This technique is mostly used by genetic testing companies who provide dietary and lifestyle advice matched to an individual's genetic profile. Lab technicians go "fishing" for specific DNA segments in order to identify genes that play a role in susceptibility to disease and that may be affected by lifestyle modifications. For example, some people may have a T instead of a C at position No. 677 of the gene called MTHFR, which plays a role in the metabolism of B vitamins. Lab technicians performing a test for this alteration will dispatch a molecular "bait" to check out position No. 677 and see whether it contains a T or a C. If they find that you have a C, then you're in luck – it is likely that you will not require B vitamins above standard recommendations. If they find you have a T, it's still not the end of the world. However, you will be advised to pay special attention to eating adequate amounts of certain B vitamin-rich foods. Testing for additional gene variants may reveal that you need to avoid certain exposures or engage in certain types of exercise – all this to compensate for the subtle alterations in your genetic code.

At the end of chapters 3 to 6, you will find examples of genes and gene variants that are currently included in this type of screening, according to various health areas.

COMPANIES CURRENTLY OFFERING NUTRIGENOMIC TESTS	
Company	**Website**
Genelex	www.genelex.com
Genovations	www.genovations.com
Integrative Therapeutics	www.integrativegenomics.com
Interleukin Genetics	www.ilgenetics.com
Market America	www.marketamerica.com
Quixtar	www.quixtar.com
Sciona*	www.sciona.com

*Includes both nutrition and genetics in analysis and recommendations. Launched in retail stores under Cellf brand.

Step 4 – Deciphering the code

Important for scientific studies, step 4 does not apply to genetic testing aimed at providing dietary and lifestyle advice – at least, not yet. This step involves "sequencing" the genes – a process that deciphers the genetic code by spelling out the "message" written into your DNA, letter by letter.

Sequencing technology has been around since the mid-1970s and won its developers the Nobel Prize in Chemistry in 1980. However, it was only in 1990 that scientists started using it to sequence all the "letters" of human DNA within the framework of the Human Genome Project. While the basic method of sequencing remained the same, what made the Project possible was the advent of new electronic and computer technologies. Instead of deciphering the DNA code manually, letter by letter, scientists were able to feed DNA samples into specially-designed machines that would create a printout of genetic "letters" – ACC GTA AAT CCG and so on – in a matter of hours.

While you may be interested in having your genes tested, you should not expect your entire genome to be spelled out in this way any time soon. Spelling out all the 3 billion letters of the human genetic code – anyone's code – is an enormous undertaking; after all, it took experts working on the Human Genome Project some 13 years (for more on the Human Genome Project see p. 12)! We are certain that someday it will be possible to send in a DNA sample and receive an unabridged genome "readout." But for the time being, the full-genome "gene cards" from the imaginary scenarios in our chapters 3 and 11 are still well in the future.

Step 5 – Interpreting the results

It's usually up to the company or institution that performed the test, or the nutritional genomics practitioner who ordered it for you, to interpret the results of your screening. Based on subtle clues in some of your genes – for example, a letter T instead of a C in a particular position – it may be possible to know how well your genes work and which dietary and lifestyle measures you need to adopt in order to maximize their function. As we've discussed throughout the book, once you have this information in hand, you can design a truly personalized strategy for long-term, optimal health.

Appendix

Gene-smart Recipes:
Flax

This appendix introduces you to flax, a plant-based source of omega-3 fats and dietary fiber. The Flax Facts text box gives you an overview of the types of flaxseed products available for home use, followed by Tips and Tricks on using flax, by author and registered dietitian Jane Reinhardt-Martin, RD. We've selected a wide variety of recipes that use flaxseed and flaxseed oil from Reinhardt-Martin's *The Amazing Flax Cookbook,* which also features Chef Ron Garrett, CEC. This cookbook is chockfull of flax facts and tasty recipes to increase your intake of omega-3 fats; it's available online at www.flaxrd.com.

FLAX FACTS

The seeds of the flax plant are rich in an omega-3 fatty acid called alpha-linolenic acid. Flaxseed contains primarily polyunsaturated fat, in the form of omega-3s, as well as a small amount of monounsaturated fat, and even less saturated fat. Flaxseed's unique components have shown potential in preventing and treating heart disease, as well as cancer, diabetes, rheumatoid arthritis, constipation and menopausal symptoms.

••• *continued* •••

FLAX FACTS *(continued)*

In addition to providing valuable omega-3 fatty acids, flaxseed also contains protein, fiber, folic acid and minerals. It is also a source of lignans that, when ingested, act like weak versions of the hormone estrogen. Lignans are thought to be helpful in preventing cancer and in relieving some of the symptoms of menopause, particularly hot flashes and night sweats.

Flaxseed is easy to use. It's available as whole flaxseed, ground flaxseed and flaxseed oil.

▸ **Whole flaxseed**
is the most economical of the three forms. The seeds come in two colors: reddish-brown and golden, both nutritionally the same. If you store the whole seeds at room temperature, they'll stay fresh for one year. Flaxseed must be ground to release the nutrients. You can purchase commercially ground flaxseed or can easily grind it at home using a coffee bean grinder. Ground seed spoils more readily than whole seed, so you should store ground seed in a tight-lidded container. Kept in a cool place, the stored seed will remain useable for up to 4 months.

▸ **Ground flaxseed**
is a convenient way to use flaxseed. Look for the terms "ground flax" or "milled flaxseed" rather than "flaxmeal" - a term indicating that some or all of the oil, which contains the valuable omega-3s, has been removed. You can store ground flaxseed for up to 4 months in a cool or cold place, in a container with a tight lid to prevent spoiling.

▸ **Flaxseed oil**
contains the omega-3s present in flaxseed but lacks the other nutrients. It should be used in cold foods and not for cooking or baking. Flaxseed oil spoils readily if kept at room temperature (in a matter of days) so refrigerate the oil and use within 6 to 8 weeks.

You can substitute flaxseed oil for part or all of the oil you would use when making a salad dressing, dip or smoothie. Ground flaxseed is particularly versatile because it can be added to cereals, casseroles, yogurt and cottage cheese, soups, stews and chili. It can also be sprinkled on salads and incorporated into baked goods.

Source: The Amazing Flax Cookbook, courtesy of author and registered dietitian Jane Reinhardt-Martin, RD, and also featuring Chef Ron Garrett, CEC. This cookbook is chockfull of flax facts and tasty recipes to increase your intake of omega-3 fats. It is available online at www.flaxrd.com.

Tips and Tricks from Jane Reinhardt-Martin, RD

Before you start trying flax recipes, there are a few basics you should master if you want to guarantee success.

▸ Measure ground flax loosely–don't pack it down into a dense mass. Otherwise, your recipe will turn out dry.

▸ Always level off your measured flax–no heaping spoons-full or overflowing cups.

▸ Unless the recipe specifically directs you to do otherwise, add your flax at the end of the cooking process. This is especially important in sauces and gravies, because flax has powerful thickening properties and can give your dishes an unpleasant consistency if you add it too early in the cooking process.

▸ Flax oil is highly unstable, and should never be subjected to high cooking temperatures. Most important–you should never use it for frying!!!

For the more adventurous among you who want to try experimenting with flax on your own, here are a couple of basic rules of substitution:

▸ When designing bakery recipes, I found that ground flax seemed to act more like a dry ingredient. So, as a general rule, cut down your flour amount by 1/2 - 3/4 cup, and add 1/2 - 3/4 cup ground flax. You will need to experiment with your recipes to obtain optimal taste.

▸ One tablespoon ground flaxseed + 3 tablespoons water replaces 1 egg. But note that you need to let the flax-water mixture "rest" for a minute or two before using it in a recipe. That way it has a chance to thicken naturally, giving you just the right consistency.

It's Not Just Your Genes!

Keep in mind that flaxseed is high in fiber. This means that it will soak up a lot of liquid. To keep your foods moist, you'll want to add extra liquid when you're adapting a traditional recipe to include flax. Add the extra liquid a few drops at a time, to avoid overdoing it.

Finally, there's the perennial problem of post-cooking clean-up. Keep in mind that flax can be pretty tenacious, once you've let it dry! To cut down on scrubbing time, make sure you pop your mixing bowls and cooking pans in for a soak (cold water seems to be more effective) as soon as possible!

Flax recipes

SALT FREE SEASONINGS

If you're watching your sodium intake, but you don't want to resign yourself to bland, unseasoned foods, flaxseed combines wonderfully well with herbs and spices to make a no-salt alternative. Here are some great blended seasonings for you to make. Just combine the ingredients in a bowl, then fill your own spice bottles with the mixtures. They also make thoughtful gifts for your culinarily inclined friends!

Herb Blend

Yield: approximately 5 tablespoons	
1-1/2 teaspoon ground sage	2-1/2 teaspoons leaf rosemary
1 tablespoon ground thyme	2 tablespoons ground flaxseed
1 tablespoon ground marjoram	

Mediterranean Blend

Yield: approximately 5 tablespoons

1 tablespoon dried dill weed or leaf basil or dried mint leaf

1 tablespoon onion powder

1/2 teaspoon leaf oregano

1/2 teaspoon celery seed

1/4 teaspoon dried lemon peel

1/8 teaspoon black pepper

2 tablespoons ground flaxseed

1/8 teaspoon allspice (optional)

Spicy Seasoning

Yield: approximately 4 tablespoons

1 tablespoon savory*

1/2 tablespoon ground mustard

1 teaspoon onion powder

1/2 teaspoon curry powder

1/2 teaspoon white pepper

1/2 teaspoon ground cumin

1/4 teaspoon garlic powder

2 tablespoons ground flaxseed

* or 1 teaspoon ground thyme and 1 teaspoon chopped mint leaf

Basic Vinaigrette

Preparation time: 5 minutes	Yield: 8 tablespoons
2 tablespoons red wine vinegar	3 tablespoons flax oil
salt, to taste	3 tablespoons extra virgin olive oil
1/8 teaspoon black pepper	

1. Place red wine vinegar, salt, and black pepper in small bowl and mix with wire whisk.

2. Add flax and olive oil, mix with wire whisk, and serve.

Per Tablespoon: Omega-3 Fats 3030 mg

Honey Mustard Dressing

Preparation time: 5 minutes	Yield: 14 tablespoons
1 tablespoon red wine vinegar	salt, to taste
1 tablespoon white wine vinegar	1/8 teaspoon black pepper
1 tablespoon fresh lemon juice	2 tablespoons plain low-fat yogurt
2 tablespoons Dijon mustard	2 tablespoons flax oil
2 tablespoons honey	2 tablespoons extra virgin olive oil

1. Place all ingredients in small bowl, except oils, and mix with wire whisk.

2. Add oils, mix with wire whisk, and serve.

Per Tablespoon: Omega-3 Fats 1154 mg

Roasted Tomato Vinaigrette

Preparation time: 60 minutes	Yield: 9 tablespoons
2 tablespoons balsamic vinegar	1/4 cup roasted tomatoes
salt, to taste	3 tablespoons flax oil
1/8 teaspoon black pepper	3 tablespoons extra virgin olive oil

1. Preheat oven at 350°.

2. Slice 2 plum or Roma tomatoes 1/4 inch thick, lay on baking sheet, season with salt and pepper, and bake tomatoes approximately 60 minutes, or till dry.

3. Let tomatoes cool before chopping.

4. Mix vinegar and chopped tomatoes in small bowl.

5. Slowly add flax and olive oil, mix with wire whisk, and serve.

Per Tablespoon: Omega-3 Fats 2694 mg

Caesar Dressing

Preparation time: 5 minutes	Yield: 10 tablespoons
1 tablespoon red wine vinegar	1/8 teaspoon black pepper
1 tablespoon white wine vinegar	3 tablespoons plain low-fat yogurt
1 tablespoon fresh lemon juice	1/4 cup fresh shredded Parmesan cheese
1 teaspoon Dijon mustard	2 tablespoons flax oil
salt, to taste	2 tablespoons extra virgin olive oil

1. Place all ingredients in small bowl, except oils, and mix with wire whisk.

2. Add flax and olive oil, mix with wire whisk, and serve.

Per Tablespoon: Omega-3 Fats 1625 mg

Bean Soup

This wonderful soup is rich in fiber, and will keep you full for several hours!!

Preparation time: 10 minutes	Cooking time: 30 minutes	Yield: 5 cups
1 tablespoon extra virgin olive oil	1/4 cup ground flaxseed	
1 medium onion, coarsely chopped	1 -15 ounce can cooked beans (Navy or Great Northern), washed and drained	
1 medium carrot, peeled and diced		
1 celery stalk, trimmed, diced	salt and pepper, to taste	
3 cloves garlic, chopped finely	Fresh chopped parsley, for garnish	
3 cups vegetable broth		

1. Preheat your stockpot, then add oil, onion, carrot, and celery. Over medium heat, saute these vegetables for 5 to 8 minutes, until the pieces are lightly browned.

2. Add the garlic, and continue to saute for another minute.

3. Add ground flaxseed and the vegetable broth, then simmer the whole mixture covered for about 15 minutes, being careful to keep the pot from reaching a boil.

4. Add beans, salt and pepper (to taste), and continue cooking for about 5 minutes more.

5. Ladle into serving bowls and garnish with fresh parsley. Accompany each bowl with a slice of whole grain bread for a satisfyingly filling meal.

Per cup: Omega-3 Fats 1633 mg | Dietary Fiber 8 g

Penne Tomato Soup

Preparation time: 10 minutes	Cooking time: 45 minutes	Yield: 8 cups

1 cup Hodgson Mill flax penne noodles, uncooked (or make your own)	2- 14.5 ounces can Italian plum tomatoes, diced
1 tablespoon unsalted butter or extra virgin olive oil	1/3 cup evaporated skim milk
	salt and pepper, to taste
1 medium onion, minced	1/3 cup Parmesan cheese, grated
1-14 ounce can vegetable broth	

1. Cook pasta according to package directions, drain, and set aside.

2. In a 3 quart saucepan, melt butter over low heat or heat olive oil, then add onions and cook about five minutes, until the pieces are translucent.

3. Add tomatoes and vegetable broth, then bring the liquid to simmer and cook for 10 minutes covered.

4. Add evaporated skim milk, stirring constantly, then continue simmering for another 5 minutes.

5. Add salt and pepper to taste, then spoon the pasta into the soup mixture.

6. Simmer another minute or so, just long enough to reheat the pasta.

7. Spoon into serving bowls, and top each with a sprinkling of grated Parmesan cheese.

Per cup: Omega-3 Fats 108 mg | Dietary Fiber 2 g

Uncle David's Marinara Sauce

My Uncle Dave came up with this variation on the traditional marinara sauce because he wanted a healthier alternative to the high-sodium, store-bought varieties. You can make it up in a large batch and freeze it so you'll always have some on hand when your family is clamoring for a spaghetti supper!

Use this sauce for the Spaghetti with Turkey Meatballs (p. 184) and Baked Tube Lasagna (p. 186).

Preparation time: 5 minutes	Cooking time: 25 minutes	Yield: 5 cups
1 tablespoon extra virgin olive oil	2 tablespoons fresh chopped parsley or parsley flakes	
4 cloves garlic, minced	1/2 teaspoon dried oregano	
1 - 28 ounce can crushed tomatoes	Salt and pepper to taste	
1 - 14.5 ounce can diced tomatoes		
1/2 teaspoon crushed red pepper flakes		

1. In a 2-quart saucepan, heat the olive oil until fragrant. Add garlic and cook on medium heat until soft.

2. Stir in both types of tomatoes and reduce heat to simmer covered for 20 minutes. Add red pepper, parsley, and oregano and simmer for about 5 more minutes. Stir occasionally, adjusting seasonings to taste.

Per cup: Omega-3 Fats 29 mg | Dietary Fiber 3 g

Spaghetti with Turkey Meatballs

Everybody loves this classic of Italian cuisine, from the seasoned gastronome to the finickiest child. What makes our version truly special are the meatballs, fortified with the great taste of flax.

Preparation time: 20 minutes	Cooking time: 40 minutes	Yield: 8 servings

Have Ready:
8 ounces Hodgson Mill flax spaghetti noodles or homemade noodles, cooked and drained

Uncle David's Marinara Sauce (p. 183)

Meatballs
8 ounces lean ground beef (round or sirloin)

8 ounces ground turkey

1/4 cup ground flaxseed

2 egg whites

3 tablespoons red wine (optional)

2 tablespoons tomato paste

salt, to taste

1/8 teaspoon black pepper

1/4 cup onion, chopped finely

1 clove garlic, chopped finely

1/2 cup shredded Parmesan cheese

1/4 cup bread crumbs

seasoned flour

2 tablespoons extra virgin olive oil

1. Mix all ingredients, except seasoned flour and oil, in large bowl together. Shape into balls. A one-inch diameter works well, but every cook has his or her own personal preference.

2. Dredge the formed balls in seasoned flour; brown in large skillet with olive oil until interior of the balls are fully cooked. Turn frequently to make certain that all sides are brown.

3. Drain pan, add marinara sauce and simmer for 10 minutes.

4. Serve over hot pasta.

Per serving: Omega-3 Fats 1408 mg | Dietary Fiber 7 g

Flax Italian Sausage

Preparation time: 5 minutes	Cooking time: 15 minutes	Yield: 1 pound
1 teaspoon granulated garlic	salt, to taste	
2 teaspoons Italian seasoning	1/2 teaspoon red pepper flakes	
2 teaspoons parsley flakes	1 pound ground turkey	
1 teaspoon black pepper	1/2 cup onion, minced	
1 teaspoon fennel seeds	1/2 cup ground flaxseed	
1/2 teaspoon leaf oregano		

1. Mix spices together first in small bowl.

2. Cook meat with onion in skillet until done, then add spices.

3. When cooked together well, take off heat, and add ground flaxseed.

Per 3 ounce serving: Omega-3 Fats 2363 mg | Dietary Fiber 4 g

Baked Tube Lasagna

This popular dish is always welcome at our table. In this version, the flax is built right into the pasta and there's even more in the sausage. To up the flax content even further, try setting out a bowl of toasted flaxseed alongside the grated Parmesan. It makes a tasty sprinkle-on topping.

Preparation time: 15 minutes	Cooking time: 45 minutes	Yield: 8 servings
1 – 12 ounce box Hodgson Mill flax penne noodles, or homemade pasta	salt and pepper, to taste	
1 cup part-skim ricotta cheese	4 ounces part-skim mozzarella cheese, shredded	
1 egg	1 pound Flax Italian Sausage (p. 185)	
1/4 cup Parmesan cheese, shredded	Uncle David's Marinara Sauce (p. 183)	

1. Preheat oven to 325°.

2. Cook pasta according to package directions, and set aside.

3. In small bowl, mix ricotta cheese, egg, and Parmesan together. Season with salt and pepper. Set aside.

4. Spray 9 x 13 pan with non-stick cooking spray.

5. Pour 1/3 of the marinara sauce into the bottom of the baking pan, spreading evenly. On top of this sauce, make a layer of the cooked pasta, using 1/2 of the total amount prepared. Top the pasta with the entire volume of cheese mixture, spreading it to the edges to form a smooth layer. Next add the sausage, again spreading it evenly. Pour half of the remaining marinara sauce over all, then create a final layer of pasta. Pour the last of the marinara on top, then add the mozzarella. Bake covered for 45 minutes.

Per serving: Omega-3 Fats 2572 mg | Dietary Fiber 10 g

Cassoulet

This dish takes long, slow cooking to bring out the complexity of its many flavors, but the end result is well worth the effort. You'll get rave reviews once family or friends sample this sophisticated French classic.

Preparation time: 30 minutes	Cooking time: 3-1/2 hours	Yield: 12 cups
1 – 16 ounce bag dry navy beans	2 tablespoons brown sugar	
2 cups reduced sodium chicken broth	salt, to taste	
12 ounces raw chicken, skinless, boneless, cut in 1-inch pieces	1/8 teaspoon ground mustard	
	1/8 teaspoon black pepper	
4 ounces ham, cut into 1-inch pieces	1 -14.5 ounce can diced tomatoes, with juice	
2 medium carrots, peeled, 1/4-inch thick pieces	1 tablespoon molasses	
1 yellow onion, coarsely chopped	2 tablespoons ketchup	
1 celery stalk, trimmed, sliced	1/2 cup toasted flaxseed	

1. Sort beans for small stones, rinse beans. Using the quick soak method, add beans to water in a large saucepan, and bring to a boil for 1-2 minutes. Take off heat and soak for 1 hour.

2. Drain off water, add the broth. Add all remaining ingredients except the flaxseed. Cover again and continue cooking on low heat another 2 to 2-1/2 hours or until the chicken is fully cooked and the beans are soft.

3. When the cassoulet mixture is ready to serve, fold in the toasted flaxseed, mixing thoroughly. Serve in a beautiful casserole dish for an impressive presentation at the table.

Per cup: Omega-3 Fats 1893 mg | Dietary Fiber 12 g

Upside-down Bacon Cheeseburger Casserole

You can call this a casserole or a savory pie. No matter what you call it, it's a real kid-pleaser, and adults love it too.

Preparation time: 15 minutes	Cooking time: 45 minutes	Yield: 6 servings
Filling:	**Crust:**	
1 pound ground turkey	2 eggs	
1 medium onion, sliced	1 cup skim milk	
1 medium bell pepper, cut into strips	1 tablespoon extra virgin olive oil	
6 sliced turkey bacon, cooked, chopped	3/4 cup all-purpose flour	
1 – 15 ounce can whole kernel corn, drained	salt, to taste	
1 - 14.5 ounce can pizza sauce, chunky style	1/8 teaspoon baking powder	
2 plum tomatoes, chopped	1/4 cup ground flaxseed	
4 ounces low-fat cheddar cheese, shredded		

1. Preheat oven to 400°.

2. In a large saucepan, brown the turkey, then add onion slices and bell pepper. Cook until the vegetables are softened and the turkey meat is fully cooked.

3. Add chopped bacon, corn, and pizza sauce to turkey mixture. Stir until the mixture is thoroughly blended.

4. Coat a 9x13 casserole dish with non-stick spray. Pour mixture into casserole dish.

••• *continued* •••

5. Add the chopped tomatoes to form a smooth layer, followed by a layer of cheese. Set casserole dish aside.

6. Place eggs in a medium mixing bowl and beat slightly. Add milk and oil, then mix in the flour, salt, baking powder, and flax, stirring until fully blended.

7. Pour the batter-like mixture over the top of the turkey mixture, spreading it to the edges of the casserole dish. Bake uncovered for 20 to 30 minutes, until the crust turns a rich, golden brown.

Per serving: Omega-3 Fats 1420 mg | Dietary Fiber 3 g

Chicken & Vegetable Stew

This dish takes a long time to cook, but don't let that put you off, because all the work is done by your slow-cooker or crock-pot. That means you're only in the kitchen for the time it takes to put the ingredients together—20 minutes, tops! To add a touch of elegance, serve it on whole-wheat toast points.

Preparation time: 20 minutes	Cooking time: 6 hours	Yield: 9 cups
1 medium onion, chopped	1 – 15 ounce can garbanzo beans, drained and rinsed	
1 bell pepper, chopped	1 – 15 ounce can tomato sauce	
1 large carrot, peeled, cut into 1/4" slices	1 – 8 ounce can sliced mushrooms, drained	
1 potato, with peel, cut into 1/2" dice	1/2 cup V-8 juice	
12 ounces skinless, boneless chicken, cut into 1" dice	1/4 cup toasted flaxseed	

1. Place all ingredients, except the flaxseed, in a crock pot. Set the pot on low and let it cook for 6 hours.

2. Just before serving, toast slices of whole-wheat bread and cut into triangles. Place two triangles at the bottom of each serving bowl, and spoon up the stew. Garnish with toasted flaxseed.

Per cup: Omega-3 Fats 1226 mg | Dietary Fiber 6 g

Meatloaf

Topping nearly everyone's list of comfort foods is the traditional meatloaf, just like mom used to make. It's a great candidate for flax-enhancement, too, because the flaxseed mixes so well with the rest of the mixture. Here's our take on this grand old dish.

Preparation time: 15 minutes	Cooking time: 1 hour	Yield: 14 pieces
2 slices whole wheat bread	1 pound ground turkey	
1/2 cup ground flaxseed	8 ounces lean ground beef	
1 large carrot, peeled and sliced	2 large eggs	
1 celery stalk, trimmed, chopped	salt, to taste	
1/2 medium onion, chopped	1 teaspoon pepper	
2 cloves fresh garlic, chopped	1 teaspoon Tabasco sauce	
1/2 cup fresh parsley, finely minced	1/2 teaspoon leaf rosemary	
3/4 cup ketchup	2 tablespoons dark brown sugar	
1-1/2 tablespoons ground mustard		

1. Preheat oven to 375°.

2. Remove crust from bread, put bread in food processer until fine.

3. Pour bread crumbs in large mixing bowl and blend in flaxseed.

4. Place carrots, celery, onion, garlic, parsley in food processor and blend until finely minced.

••• *continued* •••

5. Add vegetables to bread crumb mixture and stir in well.

6. Add 3/4 cup ketchup, 1 TBSP mustard, turkey, beef, eggs, salt, pepper, tabasco sauce, and rosemary.

7. Knead together until well blended.

8. Form into loaf and place in loaf pan (coated with non-stick spray).

9. Place remaining ketchup, mustard and brown sugar in small bowl and mix well.

10. Pour over top of meatloaf.

11. Bake at 375° for 45 minutes to 1 hour, or until internal temperature is 160°.

Per slice: Omega-3 Fats 1157 mg | Dietary Fiber 2 g

Shepherd's Pie

Ever wonder why certain foods become "comfort" foods? Because they're the foods we loved as kids. Here's our take on that great old standby, Shepherd's Pie, with a healthful twist. In place of ground beef we've gone with lower-fat turkey, and of course we've included a generous dollop of flax!

Preparation time: 10 minutes	Cooking time: 50 minutes	Yield: 8 servings

Filling:
1-1/2 pounds ground turkey

salt, to taste

1-1/2 teaspoon black pepper

2 tablespoons unsalted butter

1 large onion, minced

2 carrots, peeled and sliced

1 teaspoon garlic, minced

2 tablespoons ketchup

3 cups reduced sodium chicken broth

1/4 cup red wine (optional)

1 teaspoon Worcestershire sauce

1 teaspoon ground thyme

1 teaspoon leaf rosemary

1 cup frozen peas

6 tablespoons ground flaxseed

Topping:
2 pounds peeled russet potatoes, cut into 2-inch cubes

salt and pepper, to taste

4 tablespoons unsalted butter

3/4 cup skim milk

2 large eggs

1. Preheat oven to 400°.

2. Brown turkey in large skillet, until well done.

3. Add salt and pepper. Place ground turkey in bowl, and set aside.

••• *continued* •••

4. Place butter in saucepan, over medium heat. Add onions and carrots. Cook until tender.

5. Add garlic, and cook for 1 minute.

6. Add the remaining ingredients, except flax and peas. Bring to simmer, and add ground turkey. Cook uncovered for 15 minutes.

7. Fold in flax and peas, and remove from heat.

8. In a separate pot, cover potatoes with water, add salt, and bring to a boil.

9. Cook potatoes until tender, drain potatoes, and put back in pot. On low heat, mash potatoes, adding butter and warm milk. Blend well, add eggs.

10. Adjust seasonings.

11. Pour turkey mixture in 9x13 baking dish (coated with non-stick spray).

12. Spread mashed potatoes evenly on turkey mixture, making sure that no filling is showing.

13. Bake uncovered for 20 minutes. Let stand for about 5 minutes before serving.

Per serving: Omega-3 Fats 1675 mg | Dietary Fiber 6 g

Pecan Flax Breading

Suggested foods: chicken, salmon, red fish, catfish, pork, turkey

Preparation time: 5 minutes	Yield: 1 1/3 cups
1/2 cup plain bread crumbs	1 tablespoon dried parsley flakes or fresh chopped parsley
1/2 cup ground flaxseed	
1/4 teaspoon garlic powder	1/4 cup pecans, chopped finely
	salt, to taste
1/2 teaspoon black pepper	

Pecan Salmon with Remoulade Sauce

Preparation time: 10 minutes	Cooking time: 15 minutes	Yield: 4 servings
4 salmon fillets (4-6 ounces each)	1-2 tablespoons extra virgin olive oil	
salt and pepper, to taste	pecan flax breading (see above)	

1. Preheat oven to 350°.

2. Season salmon with salt and pepper.

3. Place in 9x13 roasting pan, which has been coated with non-stick spray.

4. Brush with olive oil.

5. Top with pecan breading mix.

6. Bake uncovered at 350° for approximately 15 minutes, or till light and flaky.

7. Serve with remoulade sauce (see following page).

Remoulade Sauce

1/2 cup low-fat mayonnaise	1 teaspoon capers, chopped
1 tablespoon Dijon mustard	1/2 teaspoon Italian seasoning

Per serving: Omega-3 Fats 4875 mg | Dietary Fiber 4 g
(for Pecan Salmon and Pecan Flax Breading–does not include Remoulade Sauce)

Mexican Flax Meat

Preparation time: 5 minutes	Cooking time: 10 minutes
1 pound ground turkey	1/2 teaspoon chili powder
1/2 medium onion, chopped	1/2 teaspoon granulated garlic <u>or</u> 1/4 teaspoon garlic powder
salt, to taste	1/2 cup ground flaxseed
1/2 teaspoon black pepper	
1/2 teaspoon cumin	

1. Brown turkey in skillet, and add onion and spices. Cook for 5 minutes.

2. Take pan off heat and mix in ground flax. Serve.

Per 3 ounce serving: Omega-3 Fats 2993 mg | Dietary Fiber 4 g

Mexican Lasagna

Preparation time: 15 minutes	Cooking time: 35-45 minutes	Yield: 6 servings
1 – 16 ounce can fat free refried beans		1/2 cup Monterey jack cheese, shredded
1 – 10 ounce can enchilada sauce		1/2 cup low-fat cheddar cheese, shredded
9 – 6 inch corn tortilla		1 – 4 ounce can diced green chilies
Mexican Flax Meat (see p. 196)		

1. Preheat oven to 350°.

2. Place refried beans and 5 ounces enchilada sauce in medium sized mixing bowl. Blend well.

3. In 9 X 13 pan (coated with non-stick spray), assemble as follows: 1/2 refried bean mixture, 3 corn tortillas, all Mexican Flax Meat, 3 corn tortillas, other 1/2 refried bean mixture, top with diced chilies, top with remaining 3 tortillas, rest of enchilada sauce, lastly shredded cheeses.

4. Bake in 350 degree oven for 35-45 minutes.

5. Let sit for about 10 minutes before cutting and serving.

Per serving: Omega-3 Fats 2665 mg | Dietary Fiber 8 g

Burrito Wraps

Preparation time: 10 minutes	Yield: 6 servings
1 – 16 ounce can fat free refried beans	1/2 cup low-fat cheddar cheese, shredded
6 – 12 inch flour tortilla	1 tomato, diced
Mexican Flax Meat (see p. 196)	salsa, optional
1 cup shredded lettuce	sour cream, optional

1. Heat refried beans till hot.

2. Lay out flour tortilla, in center place Mexican Flax Meat, lettuce, cheese, refried beans, and tomato in equal portions.

3. Fold sides to center, fold bottom up, and roll.

4. Cut diagonal. Serve with salsa and sour cream if desired.

Per serving: Omega-3 Fats 2710 mg | Dietary Fiber 10 g

Peaches & Cream

Yield: 2 cups	
1 cup skim milk	1 cup peach slices, fresh or frozen
1 cup low-fat vanilla frozen yogurt	2 tablespoons ground flax

Per cup: Omega-3 Fats 1903 mg | Dietary Fiber 4 g

Mango Shake

Yield: 2 cups	
1 cup skim milk	1 tablespoon flax oil
1-1/2 cups mango slices	1 tablespoon ground flaxseed
1 frozen banana, sliced	

Per cup: Omega-3 Fats 5006 mg | Dietary Fiber 4 g

Orange Dream

Yield: 2 cups	
1 cup skim milk	1/2 cup vanilla low-fat frozen yogurt
3 tablespoons frozen orange juice concentrate , unsweetened	2 tablespoons ground flaxseed

Per cup: Omega-3 Fats 1905 mg | Dietary Fiber 2.5 g

Taco Salad

2 ounces Mexican Flax Meat (see p. 196)	1/4 cup diced tomatoes
1-1/2 cups shredded lettuce	2 tablespoons green onion, chopped
2 tablespoons Roasted Tomato Vinaigrette dressing (see p. 179)	1/4 cup tortilla chips
	sour cream, optional
1/4 cup non-fat refried beans	
1/4 cup salsa	

1. Place lettuce on large plate or bowl and toss with dressing.

2. Top with beans and meat.

3. Garnish with salsa, tomatoes, and onion.

4. Place chips around the outside of bowl or plate, and serve.

Per serving: Omega-3 Fats 3876 mg | Dietary Fiber 19 g

California Mix Blend

1/2 cup raw broccoli florets (option steamed)

1/2 cup raw cauliflower florets (option steamed)

1/4 cup shredded carrots

1/2 cup edamame (fresh soybeans)

1 tablespoon toasted flaxseed

2 tablespoons toasted pine nuts

1 teaspoon toasted sunflower seeds

1/4 cup whole pitted black olives, sliced

2 tablespoons Honey Mustard Dressing (see p. 178)

1. Toss all ingredients in bowl and serve chilled.

Per serving: Omega-3 Fats 5332 mg | Dietary Fiber 11 g

* Source: All of the recipes are from *The Amazing Flax Cookbook*, provided courtesy of author and registered dietitian Jane Reinhardt-Martin, RD and also featuring Chef Ron Garrett, CEC.

The Amazing Flax Cookbook is available at www.flaxrd.com.

Appendix

Gene-smart Recipes:
Canyon Ranch®

W e're excited to share with you recipes from Canyon Ranch®, the fabled health resort. If you've ever questioned whether healthy food could be appealing and tasty, doubt no more!

The following recipes are surprisingly uncomplicated, exceptionally eye-appealing, and wonderfully tasty. We've selected recipes that are high in the food components you especially need if you carry gene variants we've discussed throughout this book. You'll find recipes that are low in salt and unhealthy fats and full of health-promoting components such as omega-3 fats, soy, dried beans and peas, onions and garlic, and richly-colored fruits and vegetables. Bon appétit!

The recipes are provided courtesy of Canyon Ranch® Management and Rodale, Inc., publisher of *Canyon Ranch Cooks*. This cookbook, created by Executive Chefs Barry Correia and Scott Uehlein and the kitchen staff at Canyon Ranch®, highlights a number of the scrumptious recipes served at Canyon Ranch® facilities. It's available at www.canyonranch. com, Barnes and Noble, other major bookstores, and Amazon.com.

*Rodale, Inc.   **Canyon Ranch® Management.

Arugula Salad with Roasted Tomatoes*

6 ounces cherry tomatoes, about 12 tomatoes	Makes 4 servings, each serving contains approximately:
1/4 teaspoon olive oil	-------------------------
1/4 teaspoon granulated garlic	85 calories
1/4 cup lemon juice	9 gm. carbohydrate
2 teaspoons olive oil	5 gm. fat
1/4 teaspoon salt	5 mg. cholesterol
1/4 teaspoon black pepper	5 gm. protein
2 cups fresh arugula	195 mg. sodium
2 cups mixed greens	2 gm. fiber
12 endive leaves	
4 tablespoons shredded Parmesan cheese	

1. Preheat oven to 350°. Lightly coat a small sheet pan with canola oil. Rub tomatoes with 1/4 teaspoon olive oil and sprinkle with granulated garlic. Roast in oven for 10 minutes or until just beginning to brown. Cool.

2. In a small bowl, combine lemon juice, olive oil, salt and pepper. In large bowl, combine arugula and mixed greens. Pour dressing over greens and toss lightly.

3. Plate 1 cup greens with 3 endive leaves and top with roasted cherry tomatoes. Sprinkle each salad with 1 tablespoon Parmesan cheese.

Black Bean Soup with Red Onion Salsa*

1 cup dry black beans, soaked overnight

Red Onion Salsa:
1 tablespoon minced garlic

2 teaspoons chopped cilantro

1/4 cup diced red onion

2 teaspoons red wine vinegar

1/2 cup diced onions

1/2 cup diced carrots

1/4 cup diced celery

1 medium red bell pepper, roasted and diced

1 tablespoon minced garlic

2 quarts vegetable stock (see p. 207)

1/4 teaspoon ground cumin

1/2 teaspoon salt

1 teaspoon chopped fresh oregano

2 teaspoons chopped fresh parsley

Makes 6 (3/4-cup) servings, each serving contains approximately:
----

140 calories

27 gm. carbohydrate

Trace fat

0 mg. cholesterol

8 gm. protein

182 mg. sodium

5 gm. fiber

1. In a large saucepan, cover black beans with at least 3 cups of water and soak overnight.

2. In a small bowl combine salsa ingredients. Mix well and set aside.

3. Rinse beans in a colander with fresh water and drain.

••• *continued* •••

4. Lightly spray a large saucepan with olive oil. Sauté onions, carrots, celery, roasted red pepper and 1 tablespoon garlic. Add vegetable stock and black beans. Bring to a boil, reduce heat and simmer for 1/2 to 1 hour.

5. When beans are tender, pour into blender container or food processor and puree. Add cumin, salt, oregano and parsley. Garnish with 1 tablespoon red onion salsa.

 Cook's Note: *Start with cooked canned beans and use one 15-ounce can for 1 cup dry beans. Rinse canned beans before using to reduce sodium. This will eliminate steps 1 and 3 in this recipe.*

Vegetable Stock*

Ingredients	Makes 16 (1-cup) servings, each serving contains approximately:
2 medium leeks, washed and chopped	
4 onions, chopped	
6 carrots, peeled and chopped	10 calories
1 small bunch celery, chopped	3 gm. carbohydrate
1 small bunch parsley, chopped	Trace fat
3 bay leaves	0 mg. cholesterol
2 teaspoons dried leaf marjoram	Trace protein
1/2 teaspoon dried thyme	21 mg. sodium
1 1/2 gallons cold water	Trace fiber

1. Combine all ingredients in a large pot, and bring to a boil. Reduce heat and simmer uncovered for 1 hour.

2. Line a kitchen strainer or colander with a double thickness of cheesecloth and set over a very large bowl or pot. Strain stock through cheesecloth, cool. Refrigerate or store in the freezer.

Some helpful hints for stock:
- *For sweeter tasting stock, add bell peppers, zucchini and yellow squash. (Do not add cabbage, lettuce or eggplant. This will cause bitterness. Also, do not allow vegetables to burn.)*

- *It is important to skim off any foam that comes to the surface.*

- *To prevent clouding, after initial boiling of stock, the heat should be reduced and the stock should only be allowed to simmer – never boil again. Do not cover pan.*

- *While straining, it is important to tip pan over and slowly pour liquid out, being careful not to stir up broth. This process can be accomplished using a china cap sieve lined with a coffee filter or cheesecloth.*

Tuscan Beans*

Florence is the capitol of Tuscany, and people there are so fond of beans that citizens of other regions call them mangiafagiole – literally, "bean eaters." The Florentines, a self-confident lot for centuries, choose to take it as a compliment. This dish is typical of the uncomplicated, profoundly good cooking of central Italy.

Ingredients	Makes 6 (1/2-cup) servings, each serving contains approximately:
2 teaspoons olive oil	
3/4 cups chopped onion	
3/4 cups peeled and chopped carrot	125 calories
3/4 cups chopped celery	20 gm. carbohydrate
1 teaspoon minced fresh garlic	2 gm. fat
2 cups cooked cannellini beans	3 mg. cholesterol
1/2 teaspoon each chopped, fresh sage, rosemary, oregano	8 gm. protein
2 teaspoon grated lemon peel	225 mg. sodium
1 cup chicken stock (see p. 209)	5 gm. fiber
3/4 teaspoons salt	
1/4 teaspoon black pepper	
2 tablespoons Parmesan cheese	

1. In a large sauté pan, sauté celery, carrots, onions in olive oil for 2 minutes. Add garlic, and sauté for 1 minute.

2. Lightly stir in beans, herbs, lemon peel, chicken stock, salt and pepper. Let simmer until liquid is reduced by 1/2.

3. Finish by stirring in Parmesan cheese.

Chicken Stock*

2 to 4 pounds chicken parts, except the liver	Makes 8 (1-cup) servings, each serving contains approximately:
3 quarts cold water	
2 carrots, peeled and chopped	10 calories
2 celery ribs without leaves, chopped	3 gm. carbohydrate
1 large onion cut into quarters	Trace fat
4 garlic cloves, cut into halves	1 mg. cholesterol
1 bay leaf	Trace protein
12 whole peppercorns	48 mg. sodium
	Trace fiber

1. Place chicken bones and parts in a shallow baking dish and bake in a 350° oven until golden brown, approximately 35 to 45 minutes. Drain off and discard excess fat.

2. Place browned bones and parts in a large pot, add cold water and bring to a boil. Add remaining ingredients. Reduce heat and simmer, uncovered, for 2 to 2 1/2 hours, skimming any foam that may have formed on surface. Turn off heat. Be sure not to stir stock or allow to boil again.

3. Line a kitchen strainer or colander with double thickness of cheesecloth and set over a large bowl or pot in the kitchen sink. Strain through cheesecloth, pouring slowly and steadily so as not to stir up sediment. Discard the dregs and cool.

4. Refrigerate until fat is solid on the surface. Remove fat. Refrigerate or store in small portions in the freezer.

Flax Seed Hummus Wrap**

Flax Seed Hummus

1/4 teaspoon whole coriander seed

3/4 teaspoon whole cumin seed

3 black peppercorns

1 cup canned garbanzo beans (reserve liquid)

1 tablespoon sesame tahini

2 teaspoons fresh lemon juice

1/4 teaspoon minced garlic

1 1/2 teaspoons sunflower seeds

1 teaspoon ground flax seed

1 1/2 tablespoons flax seed oil

1 teaspoon salt

1 tablespoon chopped parsley

----

4 whole-wheat tortillas, about 9-inches in diameter

1/2 avocado, cut into 4 slices

1 cucumber, cut into 16 slices

1 tomato, cut into 8 slices

1/2 cup spinach leaves

Makes 4 servings, each serving contains approximately:

----

335 calories

43 gm. carbohydrate

15 gm. fat

0 mg. cholesterol

10 gm. protein

498 mg. sodium

8 gm. fiber

1. Preheat oven to 400°. Spread whole coriander seed, cumin and peppercorns in a small pie pan. Toast in oven for 3 to 5 minutes, careful not to burn. Cool slightly. Grind in spice grinder or small coffee grinder.

2. Place all ingredients for hummus in a blender container and puree until smooth.

••• *continued* •••

3. Lay tortilla on a flat surface. Place 1/4 cup hummus, 1 slice avocado, 4 cucumber slices, 2 tomato slices and 1/4th of spinach leaves on tortilla. Roll burrito style.

Grilled Tuna Gremolata*

2 tablespoons minced fresh parsley	Makes 4 servings, each serving contains approximately:
1 tablespoon minced fresh oregano	-------------------------
1 teaspoon minced fresh garlic	160 calories
1/2 teaspoon minced lemon peel	Trace carbohydrates
------------------------------------	6 gm. fat
1 pound tuna steaks, cut into 4 equal portions	6 gm. fat
4 teaspoons olive oil	49 mg. cholesterol
1/2 teaspoon salt	26 gm. protein
1/4 teaspoon black pepper	334 mg. sodium
1 tablespoon lemon juice	Trace fiber

1. Prepare hot coals for grilling or preheat broiler.

2. Combine all ingredients for gremolata and mix well. Set aside.

3. Brush each tuna fillet with 1 teaspoon olive oil. Lightly season with salt and pepper and drizzle with lemon juice.

4. Grill or broil for 3 to 5 minutes on each side or to desired doneness.

5. Serve 2 teaspoons gremolata over each fillet.

Tabbouleh Salad**

Tabbouleh is a Middle Eastern dish, often served cold and accompanied by crisp bread such as lavosh.

1/2 cup bulgur wheat	**Makes 4 (1/2-cup) servings, each serving contains approximately:**
1 cup hot water	
1/2 cup chopped parsley	125 calories
1/4 cup chopped fresh peppermint, optional	20 gm. carbohydrate
1 medium tomato, diced	2 gm. fat
1/4 cup diced scallions	3 mg. cholesterol
1/4 cup chopped red onions	8 gm. protein
1/4 cup chopped cucumbers	225 mg. sodium
2 tablespoons olive oil	5 gm. fiber
3 tablespoons lemon juice	
1/2 teaspoon salt	
1/2 teaspoon black pepper	

1. Place bulgur in a small bowl, add hot water, cover and let soak for 20 minutes.

2. Combine bulgur with remaining ingredients and mix well.

Potato-Crusted Salmon with Dijon Shallot Sauce*

2 tablespoons minced shallots
1 teaspoon butter
1 tablespoon all-purpose flour
1/2 cup 2% milk
1/2 bay leaf
2 tablespoons white wine
1/2 teaspoon Dijon mustard
3 medium potatoes, washed, peeled and grated, about 1 pound
1 tablespoon fresh lemon juice
4 4-ounce salmon fillets

Makes 4 servings, each serving contains approximately:
----

320 calories

23 gm. carbohydrate

10 gm. fat

83 mg. cholesterol

33 gm. protein

108 mg. sodium

2 gm. fiber

1. In a medium saucepan, sauté shallots in butter over medium heat until translucent, about 1 minute. Add flour and mix with a wire whip to form a roux. Cook 1 to 2 minutes, stirring constantly, or until mixture turns light brown.

2. Slowly pour in milk and whisk until mixture comes to a boil and thickens. Add bay leaf and wine. Reduce heat to low and simmer 5 minutes. Remove from heat and add mustard.

3. Place shredded potatoes in colander and rinse several times in cold water until water is clear and starch is removed. Transfer to a large bowl and add lemon juice.

4. Preheat oven to 350°. Lightly coat an oven-proof sauté pan with olive oil.

••• *continued* •••

5. Pack 1/2 cup potato on each salmon fillet and sear, potato-side-down, in sauté pan until golden brown. Transfer to oven and bake for 8 to 10 minutes, or until salmon flakes easily.

6. Serve 1 fish fillet with 2 tablespoons of sauce.

 Cook's Note: *A roux is a mixture of flour and fat that, after being slowly cooked over low heat, is used to thicken soups and sauces.*

Mashed Cauliflower**

1 pound chopped cauliflower	Makes 8 (1/4-cup) servings, each serving contains approximately:
1 tablespoon butter	-------------------------
1 teaspoon salt	
1/4 teaspoon ground black pepper	40 calories
	3 gm. carbohydrate
	3 gm. fat
	8 mg. cholesterol
	1 gm. protein
	217 mg. sodium
	1 gm. fiber

1. In a medium saucepan, combine 1 quart of water and cauliflower. Bring to a boil and cook for 15 to 20 minutes until cauliflower is tender. Turn off heat and drain cauliflower. Add cauliflower back into warm saucepan and let sit for 1 to 2 minutes to dry cauliflower.

2. Place cauliflower into mixing bowl and add remaining ingredients. Beat with electric mixer until fluffy.

Crab Cakes with Sweet Cucumber Salsa**

1/4 cup diced red bell pepper

1/4 cup diced yellow bell pepper

1/2 cup minced red onion

2 tablespoons chopped scallions

2 tablespoons Dijon mustard

3/4 teaspoon Old Bay Seasoning

2 teaspoons Worcestershire sauce

2 tablespoons canola oil mayonnaise

1 egg yolk

3/4 cup Panko breadcrumbs

1 cup lump crab

Sweet Cucumber Salsa:
3/4 cup diced cucumbers

1/4 cup diced fresh chives

1 tablespoon diced red onion

1/3 cup diced roasted red bell peppers

1/4 cup orange marmalade

Pinch diced jalapeño pepper

1 tablespoon lime juice

Pinch salt

Makes 6 servings, each serving contains approximately:
----

135 calories

11 gm. carbohydrate

6 gm. fat

67 mg. cholesterol

8 gm. protein

408 mg. sodium

2 gm. fiber

1. Combine peppers, onions, scallions, mustard, Old Bay seasoning, Worcestershire sauce, mayonnaise, egg yolk, breadcrumbs and crab and mix well. Refrigerate for 2 hours.

••• *continued* •••

2. Combine all ingredients for sweet cucumber salsa in a medium bowl and mix well.

3. Remove crab mixture from refrigerator and portion 1/4 cup patties.

4. Lightly coat a large sauté pan with olive oil. Sauté crab cakes until golden brown on each side. Serve 2 crab cakes with 2 tablespoons sweet cucumber salsa.

Mashed Green Soybeans (Edamame)**

Ingredients	Makes 4 servings, each serving contains approximately:
1 1/2 cups edamame, shelled and steamed	
1/2 teaspoon salt	
1/2 tablespoon truffle oil	95 calories
Pinch black pepper	6 gm. carbohydrate
1/2 cup chicken or vegetable stock (see p. 207)	5 gm. fat
	0 mg. cholesterol
	7 gm. protein
	165 mg. sodium
	2 gm. fiber

1. Combine all ingredients in a blender container and puree for 2 to 3 minutes until smooth.

Spinach & Mushroom Salad with Smoked Salmon**

Soy Marinade:

1 tablespoon brown sugar

1/4 cup low-sodium tamari

3/8 cup water

1/4 teaspoon black pepper

1/4 teaspoon salt

3/4 teaspoon liquid smoke

---

4 4-ounce salmon fillets

2 tablespoons diced yellow onion

2 tablespoons olive oil

1 tablespoon champagne vinegar

1 tablespoon water

2 tablespoons brown sugar

1 tablespoon Dijon mustard

1/2 teaspoon liquid smoke

1/2 teaspoon salt

1/2 teaspoon black pepper

5 cups baby spinach

3 cups sliced mushrooms

3/4 cup diced tomatoes

1/4 teaspoon salt

Makes 4 servings, each serving contains approximately:

---

290 calories

13 gm. carbohydrate

14 gm. fat

51 mg. cholesterol

28 gm. protein

605 mg. sodium

3 gm. fiber

1. In a large bowl, combine ingredients for soy marinade. Add salmon and marinate overnight.

••• *continued* •••

2. Preheat oven to 400º. Remove salmon from marinade, wrap in foil and cook in oven for 15 to 20 minutes. Discard marinade.

3. In a small sauté pan, sauté onions in olive oil until translucent. Cool. Combine with vinegar, water, sugar, mustard, liquid smoke, salt and pepper in a blender container and puree until smooth.

4. Combine spinach, mushrooms, tomatoes and salt in a large bowl and toss well. Place 2 cups salad on plate. Top with 2 tablespoons dressing and 1 salmon fillet.

Harissa Paste**

1/2 cup dried red chili peppers	Makes 8 (1-tablespoon) servings, each serving contains approximately:
1 tablespoon olive oil	
Pinch cumin	---------------------------
Pinch dried coriander	45 calories
Pinch caraway seed	4 gm. carbohydrate
1 teaspoon minced garlic	3 gm. fat
Pinch salt	0 mg. cholesterol
	Trace protein
	279 mg. sodium
	Trace fiber

1. In a small bowl pre-soak dry chiles in hot water. Drain and chop chiles into a fine pulp and combine with olive oil in a small bowl. Add seasonings and salt. Mix well.

2. May be stored in refrigerator in covered container for several weeks.

Caramelized Vegetable and Tofu Stir-fry*

Ingredients	Nutrition
10 ounces sliced firm organic tofu	Makes 4 servings, each serving contains approximately:
2 tablespoons low-sodium tamari	-----------------------
2 tablespoons brown sugar	325 calories
Pinch chili flakes	44 gm. carbohydrate
2 teaspoons sesame tahini	12 gm. fat
1 1/2 tablespoons olive oil	0 mg. cholesterol
1 tablespoon minced garlic	19 gm. protein
1 tablespoon minced ginger root	429 mg. sodium
1 cup sliced scallions	7 gm. fiber
1 cup sliced jícama	
1 medium red bell pepper, large dice	
2 cups broccoli florets, blanched	
1 1/2 cups sliced mushrooms	
2 cups cooked chuka soba noodles	

1. Heat a wok or large sauté pan, lightly oiled, over medium high heat. Cook tofu until golden brown on each side. Remove from pan and cut into cubes.

2. In a small saucepan, combine tamari, brown sugar, chili flakes and tahini. Simmer until sugar is melted and mixture becomes a syrup, about 5 minutes. Set aside.

3. Add olive oil to wok and when hot, add garlic and ginger. Stir-fry briefly. Add remaining vegetables in order and stir-fry for about 30 seconds. Add tofu and continue to stir-fry until vegetables are tender, but crisp. Add tamari mixture and stir-fry until vegetables are coated.

4. Divide stir-fry into 4 equal portions and serve each portion over 1/2 cup cooked noodles

Moroccan Vegetable Stew with Couscous**

2 tablespoons olive oil

1 1/2 cup chopped onion

1 tablespoon minced garlic

1 teaspoon turmeric

1 cup peeled and diced Roma tomatoes

5 cups vegetable stock (see recipe p. 207)

2 cups cubed turnips

1 1/2 cups sliced carrots

1 parsley bouquet garni

1 1/2 cups cubed butternut squash

2 cups chopped cabbage

1 cup cooked garbanzo beans

1 cinnamon stick

1 teaspoon salt

1 teaspoon pepper

2 2/3 cups couscous

3 cups boiling water

1/4 teaspoon salt

1 teaspoon Harissa Paste (see recipe p. 218)

Makes 8 servings, each serving contains approximately:

350 calories

66 gm. carbohydrate

5 gm. fat

0 mg. cholesterol

11 gm. protein

452 mg. sodium

8 gm. fiber

1. Heat oil in a large saucepot. Add onions and cook for 2 to 3 minutes over medium heat until translucent. Add garlic, turmeric and tomato and cook for 2 more minutes.

••• *continued* •••

2. Add 1/2 of stock and bring to a boil. Simmer 5 minutes. Add turnips, carrots and parsley bouquet. Bring back to a simmer and cook for 15 minutes. Add squash and cabbage and cook for another 15 minutes. Add garbanzo beans, cinnamon stick and salt and pepper and remaining stock. Continue to simmer 10 to 15 more minutes.

3. Place dry couscous in a large bowl. Pour in boiling water and salt and briefly stir. Cover bowl with lid or plastic wrap to trap steam. Let sit for 10 minutes. Remove cover and fluff with a fork.

4. In a small bowl, combine 1/2 cup broth from stew with 1 teaspoon harissa paste. Serve 1/2 cup couscous with 1 1/4 cup vegetable stew and top with 2 tablespoons harissa broth (optional).

 Cook's Note: *A bouquet garni is a bundle of herbs wrapped in cheesecloth and tied with a string. In this recipe it refers to parsley only. Traditional bouquet garni has a combination of parsley, thyme and bay leaf.*

Sweet Potato Cakes with Jícama Slaw**

1 pound sweet potatoes, cleaned and pierced with a fork	Makes 6 servings, each serving contains approximately:
1/3 cup minced red bell pepper	------------------------
1/3 cup minced yellow bell pepper	380 calories
1/3 cup minced red onion	56 gm. carbohydrate
2 tablespoons chopped cilantro	15 gm. fat
3/4 teaspoon black pepper	0 mg. cholesterol
1 teaspoon ground coriander seed	10 gm. protein
1 teaspoon ground cumin	429 mg. sodium
2 1/2 teaspoons sugar	7 gm. fiber
3/4 teaspoon salt	
1 tablespoon lime juice	
1 cup breadcrumbs	
1 cup chopped pecans	

1. Preheat oven to 375°. Cut off ends of sweet potatoes and wrap in foil. Bake for 45 minutes or until soft. Let cool. Peel off skin and mash with a potato masher to a smooth consistency.

2. In a large bowl, combine sweet potatoes, peppers, onions, cilantro, spices and lime juice. Add 1/2 cup of breadcrumbs and mix well. Cover and place in refrigerator overnight.

3. In a shallow bowl, combine remaining breadcrumbs with pecans. Using 1/4 cup measure, form sweet potatoes into balls. Dredge in breadcrumb/pecan mixture and flatten.

4. Heat a large nonstick sauté pan and lightly spray with canola oil. Sauté sweet potatoes until golden brown on each side. Serve 3 patties with 1/2 cup jícama slaw (see recipe on p. 223).

Jícama Slaw**

2 medium jícama, peeled and julienned	Makes 6 (1/2-cup) servings, each serving contains approximately:
1/3 cup diced red bell pepper	-------------------------
1/4 cup chopped scallions	65 calories
1/2 cup lime juice	16 gm. carbohydrate
1/4 cup concentrated pineapple juice	Trace fat
2 tablespoons mango puree	0 mg. cholesterol
1/2 teaspoon salt	Trace protein
2 teaspoons sugar	203 mg. sodium
	Trace fiber

1. Combine jícama, red bell pepper and scallions and a large bowl.

2. Combine remaining ingredients in a medium bowl and mix well. Pour over vegetables and toss together.

Fruit and Nut Bar**

1/2 cup chopped pecans, lightly toasted	**Makes 16 bars, each containing approximately:**
1/2 cup chopped almonds, lightly toasted	-----------------------
3/4 cup honey	190 calories
2 3/4 cups rolled oats	36 gm. carbohydrate
1/2 cup dried cranberries	5 gm. fat
3/4 cup dried chopped apples	0 mg. cholesterol
1/2 cup raisins	3 gm. protein
1/2 cup sliced dates, about 10 medium	7 mg. sodium
1 teaspoon cinnamon	3 gm. fiber

1. Preheat oven to 325º. Lightly coat a 9 x 13 x 1/2-inch baking sheet with canola oil. Spread nuts on baking sheet and toast for 5 minutes.

2. Warm honey in microwave or over low heat on stovetop to the consistency of a thin syrup.

3. Place nuts in the bowl of a food processor. Chop briefly. Add oats, cranberries, apples, raisins, dates and cinnamon. Turn on machine and mix briefly until all ingredients are chopped. While machine is running, drizzle in warm honey until mixture binds.

4. Lightly spray baking sheet (same one used for nuts) with canola oil. Press mixture into baking sheet. Lightly spray parchment paper with canola oil. Using a rolling pin, roll (over parchment) until mixture is even. Place in freezer for at least 30 minutes. Cut into 16 squares.

Berry Berry Smoothie**

1/3 cup frozen raspberries	Each serving contains approximately:
1/3 cup frozen organic strawberries	-----------------------
1/2 small banana	195 calories
1/4 cup apple juice	48 gm. carbohydrate
1/4 cup cranberry nectar	Trace fat
	0 mg. cholesterol
	2 gm. protein
	5 mg. sodium
	9 gm. fiber

1. Combine all ingredients in a blender container and puree until smooth.

*Recipe from *Canyon Ranch Cooks* courtesy of Rodale, Inc.
**Recipe from Canyon Ranch® kitchens, courtesy of Canyon Ranch® Management.

Resources and Notes

·························

Sources of information on nutritional genomics

WEBSITES
Genomics/nutrigenomics centers

NuGO, The European Nutrigenomics Organization
www.nugo.org

University of California, Davis, Center of Excellence for Nutritional Genomics
www.nutrigenomics.ucdavis.edu

National Center of Excellence in Nutritional Genomics at Children's Hospital of Oakland Research Institute (CHORI)
www.chori.org/nutri_genom.html

Nutrigenomics New Zealand, Centre of Excellence in Nutrigenomics
www.nutrigenomics.org.nz

National Cancer Institute, National Institutes of Health, Cancer Genome Atlas
http://cancergenome.nih.gov

Pennsylvania State University, Center of Excellence in Nutrigenomics
www.nutrigenomics.psu.edu

US National Human Genome Research Institute (NHGRI)
www.genome.gov

WEBSITES
National health organizations and government agencies
American Dietetic Association (ADA)
www.eatright.org

American Diabetes Association
www.diabetes.org

American Institute for Cancer Research (AICR)
www.aicr.org

It's Not Just Your Genes!

Centers for Disease Control and Prevention (CDC)
www.cdc.gov

Department of Energy (US), Oak Ridge National Laboratory
www.ornl.gov/sci/techresources/Human_Genome/home.shtml

Dietitians of Canada
www.dietitians.ca

National Heart, Lung, and Blood Institute (NHLBI)
www.nhlbi.nih.gov

National Institutes of Health (NIH)
www.nih.gov

BOOKS:
DeBusk R, Joffe Y. *It's Not Just Your Genes!* San Diego, CA: BKDR, Inc.; 2006.

DeBusk RM. *Genetics: The Nutrition Connection.* Chicago, IL: the American Dietetic Association; 2003.

Heber D. *What Color is Your Diet?* New York: HarperCollins/Regan Books; 2001.

Simopolous AP, Robinson J. *The Omega Diet.* New York, NY: HarperCollins; 1999.

Correia B, Uehlein S, Kitchen Staff of Canyon Ranch®. *Canyon Ranch Cooks.* New York, NY: Rodale, Inc.; 2001.

Reinhardt-Martin J. *The Amazing Flax Cookbook.* Moline, IL: TSA Press; 2004.

Notes

CHAPTER 1
P. 5 **Jim Fixx:** Website of sports writer Hal Higdon, www.halhigdon.com/Articles/Fixx. htm. Accessed September 15, 2005.

P. 6 **he answered in two words: "No sport":** Morris D. Prevention Better Than Cure? The Key to Longevity: Activity without Anxiety. *Future – The Aventis Magazine,* 2/2003, p. 7.

P. 7 **Some researchers claimed all the hereditary information:** Colin Tudge. *In Mendel's Footnotes.* London: Vintage, 2002, pp. 44-50.

P. 8 **spent eight years breeding pea plants:** *Ibid.*, p.75.

P. 8 **Mendel's work was rediscovered around 1900:** *Ibid.*, p. 76.

P. 8 **The word "gene" ... was coined:** The Human Genome Project Timeline. Website of the National Human Genome Research Institute, National Institutes of Health, www.genome.gov/Pages/Education/Kit/main.cfm?pageid=24. Accessed August 1, 2005.

P. 8 **Archibald Garrod:** Website of the J. Craig Venter Institute's Genome News Network, www.genomenewsnetwork.org/resources/timeline/1908_Garrod.php. Accessed September 16, 2005.

P. 9 **"solved the secret of life":** James Watson. *The Double Helix.* The New American Library, New York, 1969, p. 126.

P. 9 **"too pretty not to be true":** *Ibid.,* p. 134.

P. 9 **virtually all organisms:** The Discovery of the Molecular Structure of DNA - The Double Helix. Website of the Nobel Foundation, http://nobelprize.org/medicine/educational/dna_double_helix. Accessed August 1, 2005.

P. 10 **An average gene has about 3,000:** Human Genome Project Information, website funded by the US Department of Energy Office of Science www.ornl.gov/sci/techresources/Human_Genome/project/info.shtml. Accessed November 5, 2005.

P. 11 **only 20,000 to 25,000 genes:** Stein LD. Human genome: end of the beginning. *Nature* 2004;431:915-916.

P. 12 **99.9 percent of human DNA is identical in all of us:** Human Genome Project Information. Website funded by the US Department of Energy Office of Science, www.ornl.gov/sci/techresources/Human_Genome/home.shtml. Accessed August 1, 2005.

CHAPTER 2
For a more detailed discussion on this topic, see Ruth DeBusk. Genetics: The Nutrition Connection. Chicago, IL: The American Dietetic Association, 2003.

P. 17 **"Genes, like diamonds":** Richard Dawkins. *The Selfish Gene.* Oxford University Press, 1989, p. 35.

P. 21 **Gamma-linolenic acid:** Menendez JA, Vellon L, Colomer R, Lupu R. Effect of gamma-linolenic acid on the transcriptional activity of the Her-2/neu (erbB-2) oncogene. *J Natl Cancer Inst* 2005;97(21):1611-1615.

CHAPTER 3

P. 26 **1 million; 3 million; 2.5 billion; 60,000:** *Yale University School of Medicine Heart Book.* New York: Hearst Books, 1992, p. 4.

P. 26 **64 million; 50 million; close to 1 million; $500 billion:** 2004 Morbidity and Mortality Chartbook. Website of the National Heart, Lung and Blood Institute, www.nhlbi.nih.gov/resources/docs/cht-book.htm. Accessed September 4, 2005.

P. 26 **12 million:** World Health Organization. *World Health Report 2002. Reducing Risks, Promoting Healthy Life.* Geneva: WHO. Quoted in: Ordovas J. The quest for cardiovascular health in the genomic era: nutrigenetics and plasma lipoproteins. *Proc Nutr Soc* 2004;63:145-152.

P. 25 **on average only one case a month:** McCrae T. *Osler's Principles and Practice of Medicine.* London: Appleton. 1912, p. 836. Quoted in: Ordovas J. The quest for cardiovascular health in the genomic era: nutrigenetics and plasma lipoproteins. *Proc Nutr Soc* 2004;63:145-152.

P. 26 **According to some theories, deep within our genetic code:** Cordain L, Eaton SB, Sebastian A, et al. Origins and evolution of the Western diet: health implications for the 21st century. *Am J Clin Nutr* 2005;81(2):341-354; O'Keefe JH Jr, Cordain L. Cardiovascular disease resulting from a diet and lifestyle at odds with our Paleolithic genome: how to become a 21st-century hunter-gatherer. *Mayo Clin Proc* 2004;79(1):101-108.

P. 27 **striking differences in the way people respond to dietary measures:** Ordovas JM. The quest for cardiovascular health in the genomic era: nutrigenetics and plasma lipoproteins. *Proc Nutr Soc* 2004;63:145-152.

P. 27 **Several hundred genes are thought to be involved:** Ordovas JM. Gene-diet interaction and plasma lipid responses to dietary intervention. *Biochem Soc Trans* 2002;30(2):68-73.

P. 27 **a gene called APOA1 ... is involved in regulating:** *Ibid.*

P. 28 **the advice of the American government:** Dietary Guidelines for Americans 2005. Department of Health and Human Services and Department of Agriculture. Website of US government health initiatives, www.healthierus.gov/dietaryguidelines. Accessed September 7, 2005.

P. 28 **susceptible to the harmful effects of smoking:** Corella D, Guillen M, Carmen Saiz C, et al. Associations of *LPL* and *APOC3* gene polymorphisms on plasma lipids in a Mediterranean population: interaction with tobacco smoking and the *APOE* locus. *J Lipid Res* 2002;43:416-427.

P. 28 **appears to reverse the usual protective effects of moderate drinking:** Djousse L, Pankow JS, Arnett DK, et al. Apolipoprotein E polymorphism modifies the alcohol-HDL association observed in the National Heart, Lung, and Blood Institute Family Heart Study. *Am J Clin Nutr* 2004;80(6):1639-44.

P. 28 **it is people with E4 – and not those with E2 and E3 – who can most effectively:** Corella D, Ordovas JM. Single nucleotide polymorphisms that influence lipid metabolism: interaction with dietary factors. *Annu Rev Nutr* 2005;25:341-390.

P. 31 **Over 83 percent of people who die of coronary heart disease:** Website of the American Heart Association, www.americanheart.org/presenter.jhtml?identifier=500. Accessed September 6, 2005.

P. 31 **About half of heart attacks and other cardiovascular problems occur:** Rifai N, Ridker PM. Inflammatory markers and coronary cardiovascular disease. *Curr Opin Lipidol* 2002;13(4):383-389.

P. 30 **statins may offer extra protection because:** Chasman DI, Posada D, Subrahmanyan L, et al. Pharmacogenetic study of statin therapy and cholesterol reduction. *JAMA* 2004;291(23):2821-2827; Ridker PM. High-sensitivity C-reactive protein, inflammation, and cardiovascular risk: from concept to clinical practice to clinical benefit. *Am Heart J* 2004;148(1 Suppl):S19-26.

P. 30 **the beneficial effects of aspirin:** Ridker PM, Cushman M, Stampfer MJ, et al. Inflammation, aspirin, and the risk of cardiovascular disease in apparently healthy men. *N Engl J Med* 1997;336(14):973-979.

P. 30 **high CRP levels can predict:** Ridker PM, Rifai N, Rose L, et al. Comparison of C-reactive protein and low-density lipoprotein cholesterol levels in the prediction of first cardiovascular events. *N Engl J Med* 2002;347(20):1557-1565.

P. 30 **One of the variants of the IL-6 gene, referred to as -174G>C:** Humphries SE, Luong LA, Ogg MS, et al. The interleukin-6 -174 G/C promoter polymorphism is associated with risk of coronary heart disease and systolic blood pressure in healthy men. *Eur Heart J* 2001;22:2243-2252.

P. 30 **Cigarette smoke, which stimulates the IL-6 gene, exerts a particularly strong effect:** *Ibid.*

P. 32 **inflammatory response might have provided an evolutionary advantage:** Kornman KS, Martha PM, Duff GW. Genetic variations and inflammation: a practical nutrigenomics opportunity. *Nutrition* 2004;20(1):44-49.

P. 32 **homocysteine can build up to dangerously high levels, increasing the risk:** Wald DS, Low M, Morris JK. Homocysteine and cardiovascular disease: evidence on causality from a meta-analysis. *BMJ* 2002;325:1202-1209.

P. 34 **about half of Caucasians and Asians have one copy of the 677C>T variant:** Bailey LB, Gregory JF. Polymorphisms of methylenetetrahydrofolate reductase and other enzymes: metabolic significance, risks and impact on folate requirement. *J Nutr* 1999;129:919-922.

P. 34 **when such individuals have a diet low in folate:** de Bree A, Verschuren WM, Bjorke-Monsen AL, et al. Effect of the methylenetetrahydrofolate reductase 677C-->T mutation on the relations among folate intake and plasma folate and homocysteine concentrations in a general population sample. *Am J Clin Nutr* 2003;77(3):687-693.

P. 35 **Centuries ago in Africa, giant camel caravans:** Derek Denton. *Hunger for Salt.* Springer-Verlag, 1982. Quoted in: The Why Files, http://whyfiles.org/111salt/index.html. Accessed September 5, 2005.

P. 36 **health authorities strongly recommend a reduced-salt diet:** Your Guide to Lowering High Blood Pressure. Website of the National Heart, Lung and Blood Institute, www.nhlbi.nih.gov/hbp/prevent/sodium/sodium.htm. Accessed September 5, 2005.

P. 36 **hypertension – the leading cause of strokes and a major risk factor for heart attacks:** *Yale University School of Medicine Heart Book,* p. 149.

P. 38 **In one large study in the United States, 1,500 subjects:** Hunt SC, Cook NR, Oberman A, et al. Angiotensinogen genotype, sodium reduction, weight loss, and prevention of hypertension: trials of hypertension prevention, phase II. *Hypertension* 1998;32(3):393-401.

P. 39 **more than 60 percent of Americans don't get enough exercise:** Chronic Disease Prevention. Website of Centers for Disease Control and Prevention, www.cdc.gov/nccdphp/aag/aag_dnpa.htm. Accessed September 7, 2005.

P. 39 **Approximately 250,000 deaths:** Website of the American Heart Association, www.americanheart.org/presenter.jhtml?identifier=820. Accessed September 7, 2005.

P. 39 **Being overweight not only increases the risk of heart disease:** Ordovas JM. The quest for cardiovascular health in the genomic era: nutrigenetics and plasma lipoproteins. *Proc Nutr Soc* 2004;63:145-152.

P. 42 **This relative decline might be partly responsible:** Simopoulos AP. The importance of the ratio of omega-6/omega-3 essential fatty acids. *Biomed Pharmacother* 2002;56:365-379.

CHAPTER 4

P. 49 **The longest-living person on record:** Guinness World Records, www.guinness-worldrecords.com. Accessed August 30, 2005.

P. 50 **up to ten alterations must accumulate in a single cell:** What the Weizmann Institute is Doing about Cancer. 2004. Publications and Media Relations Department, Weizmann Institute of Science.

P. 51 **have an exceptionally high chance of developing breast or ovarian cancer by age 70:** Breast Cancer. Risk Factors. Website of Memorial Sloan-Kettering Cancer Center, www.mskcc.org/mskcc/html/293.cfm. Accessed July 21, 2005

P. 51 **only about 5 percent match this genetic profile:** *Ibid.*

P. 52 **According to the journal** *Science,* **only about 5 percent:** Perera FP. Environment and cancer: who are susceptible? *Science* 1997;278:1068-1073.

P. 52 **Breast cancer rates in the United States are four to seven times higher:** Ziegler RG, Hoover RN, Pike MC, et al. Migration patterns and breast cancer risk in Asian-American women. *J Natl Cancer Inst* 1993;85(22):1819-1827.

P. 55 **One study by California researchers:** Lin HJ, Probst-Hensch NM, Louie AD, et al. Glutathione transferase null genotype, broccoli, and lower prevalence of colorectal adenomas. *Cancer Epidemiol Biomarkers Prev* 1998;7(8):647-652.

P. 58 **a 1999 study reported in the journal** *Cancer Research:* Ambrosone CB, Freudenheim JL, Thompson PA, et al. Manganese superoxide dismutase (MnSOD) genetic polymorphisms, dietary antioxidants, and risk of breast cancer. *Cancer Res* 1999;59(3):602-606.

P. 58 **at least half of all cancer deaths could be avoided:** Website of the American Cancer Society, www.cancer.org. Accessed July 21, 2005

P. 60 **a recent review of medical literature suggests:** Lee IM. Physical activity and cancer prevention: data from epidemiologic studies. *Med Sci Sports Exerc* 2003;35(11):1823-1827.

CHAPTER 5

P. 67 **The Pima Indians who live in the Sonaran have a dubious distinction:** Ravussin E, Valencia ME, Esparza J, et al. Effects of a traditional lifestyle on obesity in Pima Indians. *Diabetes Care* 1994;17:1067-1074; Pratley RE. Gene-environment interactions in the pathogenesis of type 2 diabetes mellitus: lessons learned from the Pima Indians. *Proc Nutr Soc* 1998;57:175-181; Bennett PH. Type 2 diabetes among the Pima Indians of Arizona: an epidemic attributable to environmental change? *Nutr Rev* 1999;57:S61-54; Valencia ME, Bennett PH, Ravussin E, et al. The Pima Indians in Sonora, Mexico. *Nutr Rev* 1999;57:S55-58.

P. 68 **From 1980 to 2005, the number of Americans with diabetes more than doubled:** Diabetes: Disabling, Deadly, and on the Rise. Website of the Centers for Disease Control and Prevention, www.cdc.gov/nccdphp/publications/aag/ddt.htm. Accessed December 6, 2005.

P. 68 **more than 20 million:** Website of the National Diabetes Information Clearinghouse (NDIC), a service of the National Institute of Diabetes and Digestive and Kidney Diseases, National Institutes of Health, http://diabetes.niddk.nih.gov/index.htm. Accessed November 29, 2005.

P. 68 **estimated to be around 200 million:** Website of the International Diabetes Federation, www.idf.org/home/index.cfm?node=264. Accessed December 6, 2005.

P. 68 **affecting about 330 million people by 2025:** *Ibid.*

P. 69 **Dr. Neel argued that, for thousands of years:** Neel JV. When some fine old genes meet a 'new' environment. Simopoulos AT, ed. Aspects of Nutrition and Health. Diet, Exercise, Genetics and Chronic Disease. *World Rev Nutr Diet* Basel: Karger. 1999;84:1-18.

P. 70 **among overweight American teens, as many as one in six have abnormally high:** Williams DE, Cadwell BL, Cheng YJ, et al. Prevalence of impaired fasting glucose and its relationship with cardiovascular disease risk factors in US adolescents, 1999-2000. *Pediatrics* 2005;116(5):1122-1126.

P. 71 **you have a 40 percent chance of eventually developing the disease:** Barroso I. Genetics of type 2 diabetes. *Diabet Med* 2005;22:528.

P. 71 **is still only between 50 to 90 percent:** Permutt MA, Wasson J, Cox N. Genetic epidemiology of diabetes. *J Clin Invest* 2005; 115:1431-1439.

P. 72 **Risk factors associated with the metabolic syndrome include:** Groop L. Genetics of the metabolic syndrome. *Br J Nutr* 2000;83(1):39-48.

P. 72 **experts think there is probably no such gene:** Barroso I. Genetics of type 2 diabetes. *Diabet Med* 2005;22:528.

P. 73 **drugs that improve insulin sensitivity (the thiazolidenediones, or TZDs):** Franks PW, Luan J, Browne PO, et al. Does peroxisome proliferator-activated receptor gamma genotype (Pro12ala) modify the association of physical activity and dietary fat with fasting insulin level? *Metabolism* 2004;53(1):11-16.

P. 73 **A certain form of this gene, referred to as Pro12Ala, seems to be protective:** *Ibid.*

P. 73 **in one study, only 1.9 percent of African Americans:** Kao WH, Coresh J, Shuldiner AR, et al. Pro12Ala of the peroxisome proliferator-activated receptor-gamma2 gene is associated with lower serum insulin levels in nonobese African Americans: the Atherosclerosis Risk in Communities Study. *Diabetes* 2003;52(6):1568-1572.

P. 74 **when people ate a significantly greater amount of polyunsaturated than saturated fats, the protective variant of the PPAR-gamma gene:** Luan J, Browne PO, Harding AH, et al. Evidence for gene-nutrient interaction at the PPARgamma locus. *Diabetes* 2001;50(3):686-689.

P. 74 **In 1996, a study of Mexican Americans in Starr County, Texas:** The Genetic Landscape of Diabetes. Website of the National Center for Biotechnology Information, www.ncbi.nlm.nih.gov/books/bv.fcgi?rid=diabetes.section.631. Accessed November 2, 2005.

P. 75 **in 2005 researchers published a study of some 2,300 people in Finland:** Lyssenko V, Almgren P, Anevski D. Genetic prediction of future type 2 diabetes. *PLoS Medicine* 2005;2(12):e345.

P. 75 **increased 20-fold in women with a body mass index of more than 30:** Permutt MA, Wasson J, Cox N. Genetic epidemiology of diabetes. *J Clin Invest* 2005; 115:1431-1439.

P. 77 **Diabetes Prevention Program:** Diabetes Prevention Program Research Group. Reduction in the incidence of type 2 diabetes with lifestyle intervention or metformin. *N Engl J Med* 2002:346:393-403.

P. 77 **Even a moderate weight loss – about 5 percent of body weight:** *Ibid.* and Reaven GM. The insulin resistance syndrome: definition and dietary approaches to treatment. *Annu Rev Nutr* 2005;25:391-406.

CHAPTER 6

P. 81 **researchers from nearby Creighton University:** Rapuri PB, Gallagher JC, Kinyamu HK, Ryschon KL. Caffeine intake increases the rate of bone loss in elderly women and interacts with vitamin D receptor genotypes. *Am J Clin Nutr* 2001:74, 694-700.

P. 83 **30 is the beginning of the end:** Website of the National Institutes of Health, Osteoporosis and Related Bone Diseases, National Resource Center, www.osteo.org. Accessed November 29, 2005.

P. 84 **one in two people who fractures a hip never resumes his or her former lifestyle, and as many as one in four die within a year:** Physical Activity, Nutrition and Bone Health. International Food Information Council Foundation. Washington, DC, 2002. Available at www.ific.org. Accessed October 27, 2005.

P. 84 **More than 1.5 million fractures in the United States:** Website of the National Institutes of Health, Osteoporosis and Related Bone Diseases, National Resource Center, www.osteo.org. Accessed November 29, 2005.

P. 85 **According to the National Osteoporosis Foundation, there are an estimated 10 million:** Website of the National Osteoporosis Foundation, www.nof.org. Accessed July 11, 2005.

P. 85 **Back in the 1970s and 1980s, studies with twins:** Gennari L, Becherini I, Falchetti A, et al. Genetics of osteoporosis: role of steroid hormone receptor gene polymorphisms. Review. *J Steroid Biochem Mol Biol* 2001;81:1-24.

P. 86 **women of Caucasian and Asian ancestry are at a greater risk:** Website of the National Institutes of Health, Osteoporosis and Related Bone Diseases, National Resource Center, www.osteo.org. Accessed November 29, 2005.

P. 87 **in 2002, scientists from the China Medical College in Taiwan:** Chen HY, Chen WC, Hsu CD, Tsai F J, and Tsai CH. Relation of Vitamin D receptor FokI start codon polymorphism to bone mineral density and occurrence of osteoporosis in postmenopausal women in Taiwan. *Acta Obstet Gynecol Scand* 2002;81:93-98.

P. 88 **a study conducted at the Garvan Institute:** Brown MA, Haughton MA, Grant SF, et al. Genetic control of bone density and turnover: role of the collagen 1alpha1, estrogen receptor, and vitamin D receptor genes. *J Bone Miner Res* 2001;16:758-764.

P. 88 **while thanking your lucky Starbucks®:** Starbucks® is a registered trademark of Starbucks Corporation.

P. 89 **People with certain variants of the gene called COL1A1:** Hobson EE and Ralston SH. Role of genetic factors in the pathophysiology and management of osteoporosis. *Clin Endocrinol (Oxf)* 2001;54:1-9.

P. 89 **The good news is that this gene variant's adverse effect:** Brown MA, Haughton MA, Grant SF, et al. Genetic control of bone density and turnover: role of the collagen 1alpha1, estrogen receptor, and vitamin D receptor genes. *J Bone Miner Res* 2001;16:758-764.

P. 90 **One variant of TNF-alpha – referred to as -308G>A – has been associated:** Ota N, Hunt SC, Nakajima T, et al. Linkage of human tumor necrosis factor-alpha to human osteoporosis by sib pair analysis. *Genes Immun* 2000;1:260-264.

P. 90 **IL-6 gene variant called -174G>C:** Ferrari S. Genetics, Nutrition and Bone Health. In *Nutrition and Bone Health.* Edited by Michael Holick and Bess Dawson-Hughes. Totowa, NJ: Humana Press Inc., 2004, pp. 19-41.

P. 94 **According to noted vitamin D researcher Michael Holick, MD, PhD:** Grant WB, Holick MF. Benefits and requirements of vitamin D for optimal health: a review. *Altern Med Rev* 2005;10:94-111.

CHAPTER 7

P. 101 **In a study published in 2000, researchers from Charles University in Prague:** Hainer V, Stunkard AJ, Kunesova M, et al. Intrapair resemblance in very low calorie diet-induced weight loss in female obese identical twins. *Int J Obes Relat Metab Disord* 2000;24(8):1051-7.

P. 102 **the risk of becoming obese is on average two to three times higher:** Loos RJF, Bouchard C. Obesity – is it a genetic disorder? *J Int Med* 2003;254:401-425.

P. 102 **the risk soars to seven or eight times the normal level:** *Ibid.*

P. 104 **Dietary Guidelines for Americans 2005:** Website of US government health initiatives, www.health.gov/dietaryguidelines/dgac/pdf/2kdiet.pdf. Accessed November 26, 2005.

P. 105 **In the 1930s, American insurance companies:** Speakman JR. Obesity: the integrated roles of environment and genetics. *J Nutr* 2004;134:2090S-2105S.

P. 105 **obese people tend to die at a younger age:** *Ibid.*

P. 105 **the risk of contracting this disease is *40 to 90* times greater:** Ibid.

P. 105 **Obesity also increases the risk of heart disease, stroke, certain forms of cancer:** *Ibid.*

P. 105 **More than 75 percent of high blood pressure cases:** F as in Fat: How Obesity Policies are Failing in America. 2005. Website of the Trust for America's Health, http://healthyamericans.org/reports/obesity2005/Obesity2005Report.pdf. Accessed November 25, 2005.

P. 105 **obesity will soon overtake smoking as the leading risk factor:** Mokdad AH, Marks JS, Stroup DF, Gerberding JL. Actual causes of death in the United States, 2000. *JAMA* 2004;291(10):1238-1245.

P. 107 **Hippocrates ... advised the obese to "eat only once a day":** Friedman JF. Modern science versus the stigma of obesity. *Nat Med* 2004;10(6):563-569.

P. 107 **our genetic make-up ... has changed little over the past 50,000 years or so:** Neel JV. When some fine old genes meet a 'new' environment. Simopoulos AT, ed. Aspects of Nutrition and Health. Diet, Exercise, Genetics and Chronic Disease. *World Rev Nutr Diet* Basel: Karger. 1999;84:1-18.

P. 108 **24 percent of Aboriginal males and 27 percent of Aboriginal women are classified as obese:** Cunningham J and Mackerras D. Overweight and obesity: indigenous Australians. Australian Bureau of Statistics. 1998. www.ausstats.abs.gov.au/Ausstats/free.nsf/Lookup/ECB3E89F6356B5B9CA256AD9001CFDA7/$File/47020.pdf. Accessed November 5, 2005.

P. 109 **adopted children were more likely to have a BMI similar:** Maes HHM, Neale MC, Eaves LJ. Genetic and environmental factors in relative body weight and human adiposity. *Behavior Genetics* 1997; 27(4):325-351.

P. 109 **Similar evidence for the role of genetics comes from twin studies:** *Ibid.*

P. 109 **lipostat theory:** Speakman JR. Obesity: the integrated roles of environment and genetics. *J Nutr* 2004;134:2090S-2105S.

P. 110 **obese mouse born in a US laboratory in the 1950s:** *Ibid.*

P. 110 **another group of scientists identified the gene responsible for this mouse's obesity:** *Ibid.*

P. 111 **In human trials, however, these hopes started to falter:** Chicurel M. Whatever happened to leptin? *Nature* 2000;404:538-540.

P. 112 **scientists analyzed the report of the Quebec Overfeeding Study:** Ukkola O, Bouchard C. Role of candidate genes in the response to long-term overfeeding: review of findings. *Obes Rev* 2004;5:3-12.

P. 113 **In a 2003 study conducted at the same Canadian university:** Garenc C, Perusse L, Chagnon YC, et al. Effects of beta2-adrenergic receptor gene variants on adiposity: the HERITAGE Family Study. *Obes Res* 2003;11(5):612-618.

P. 113 **a number of studies have shown that people with a G version of this gene:** Loos RJF and Rankinen T. Gene-diet interactions on body weight changes. *J Am Diet Assoc* 2005;105(5):S29-34.

P. 113 **people with a G version ... have less success in weight-loss programs:** Fumeron F, Durack-Bown I, Betoulle D, et al. Polymorphisms of uncoupling protein (UCP) and beta 3 adrenoreceptor genes in obese people submitted to a low calorie diet. *Int J Obes Relat Metab Disord* 1996;20(12):1051-1054.

P. 113 **Australian researchers recently put two groups of overweight and obese people:** Noakes M, Keogh JB, Foster PR, Clifton PM. Effect of an energy-restricted, high-protein, low-fat diet relative to a conventional high-carbohydrate, low-fat diet on weight loss, body composition, nutritional status, and markers of cardiovascular health in obese women. *Am J Clin Nutr* 2005;81(6):1298-1306.

P. 114 **Researchers from the United States and Spain studied different variants of a gene called PLIN:** Corella D, Qi L, Sorli JV, et al. Obese subjects carrying the 11482G>A polymorphism at the perilipin locus are resistant to weight loss after dietary energy restriction. *J Clin Endocrinol Metab* 2005;90(9):5121-5126.

P. 115 **In 1931, chemists at DuPont were experimenting:** Melissa Lee Phillips. Scientists Find Bitter Taste Gene. From: Neuroscience for Kids, popular science website created by Dr. Eric Chudler, University of Washington. http://faculty.washington.edu/chudler/bitter.html. Accessed November 4, 2005.

P. 115 **Studies show that in the adult Caucasian population in North America:** Tepper BJ. 6-n-Propylthiouracil: a genetic marker for taste, with implications for food preference and dietary habits. *Am J Hum Genet* 1998;63(5):1271-1276.

P. 116 **in one study of middle-aged women:** Goldstein GL, Daun H, Tepper BJ. Adiposity in middle-aged women is associated with genetic taste blindness to 6-n-propylthiouracil. *Obes Res* 2005;13(6):1017-1023.

P. 116 **non-taster preschool children were more likely:** Keller KL, Steinmann L, Nurse RJ, Tepper BJ. Genetic taste sensitivity to 6-n-propylthiouracil influences food preference and reported intake in preschool children. *Appetite* 2002;38(1):3-12.

P. 117 **inflammatory substances ... may at least partly be responsible:** Hotamisligil GS. Inflammatory pathways and insulin action. *Int J Obes Relat Metab Disord* 2003;27 (Suppl 3):S53-55.

P. 117 **TNF-alpha ... has been specifically associated with type 2 diabetes:** Hotamis-ligil GS, Spiegelman BM. Tumor necrosis factor alpha: a key component of the obesity-diabetes link. *Diabetes* 1994;43:1271-1278.

P. 117 **Studies suggest that giving mice TNF-alpha:** Moller DE. Potential role of TNF-alpha in the pathogenesis of insulin resistance and type 2 diabetes. *Trends Endocrinol Metab* 2000;11:212-217.

P. 117 **bulimia and binge eating, have also been shown to be linked to genes:** Bulik CM, Tozzi F. The genetics of bulimia nervosa. *Drugs Today (Barc)* 2004 Sep;40(9):741-749. Potoczna N, Branson R, Kral JG, et al. Gene variants and binge eating as predictors of comorbidity and outcome of treatment in severe obesity. *J Gastrointest Surg* 2004 8(8):971-981.

P. 117 **physicians and scientists from Switzerland, Germany and the United States studied:** Branson R, Potoczna N, Kral JG, et al. Binge eating as a major phenotype of melanocortin 4 receptor gene mutations. *N Engl J Med* 2003;348(12):1096-1103.

P. 118 **a modest weight loss of 5 to 10 pounds can improve our health:** Tuomilehto J, Lindstrom J, Eriksson JG, et al. Prevention of type 2 diabetes mellitus by changes in lifestyle among subjects with impaired glucose tolerance. *N Engl J Med* 2001;344(18):1343-1350.

CHAPTER 8

P. 121 **A notable example is Eero Mäntyranta:** McCrory P. Super athletes or gene cheats? *Br J Sports Med* 2003;37:192-193.

P. 122 **there are other gene variants affecting athletic performance:** Heck AL, Barroso CS, Callie ME, Bray MS. Gene-nutrition interaction in human performance and exercise response. *Nutrition* 2004;20:598-602.

P. 123 **Data on world-class decathletes:** Van Damme R, Wilson RS, Vanhooydonck B, Aerts P. Performance constraints in decathletes. *Nature* 2002;415(6873):755-756.

P. 123 **"power" types will increase the bulk of their muscles:** Folland J, Leach B, Little T, et al. Angiotensin-converting enzyme genotype affects the response of human skeletal muscle to functional overload. *Exp Physiol* 2000;85(5):575-579.

P. 123 **In one British study, the ACE gene variants were:** Montgomery HE, Marshall R, Hemingway H, et al. Human gene for physical performance. *Nature* 1998;393:221-222.

P. 123 **In another study by the same researchers:** *Ibid.*

P. 124 **In an Australian study, researchers screened ... for variants of a gene called ACTN3:** Yang N, MacArthur DG, Gulbin JP, et al. ACTN3 genotype is associated with human elite athletic performance. *Am J Hum Genet* 2003;73:627-631.

P. 124 **A recent review lists more than 100 genes:** Rankinen T, Perusse L, Rauramas R, et al. The human gene map for performance and health-related fitness phenotypes: the 2003 update. *Med Sci Sports Exerc* 2004;36(9):1451-1469.

P. 125 **an Australian study has revealed that the activity of a gene that helps glucose:** Kraniou Y, Cameron-Smith D, Misso M, et al. Effects of exercise on GLUT-4 and gly-cogenin gene expression in human skeletal muscle. *J Appl Physiol* 2000;88(2):794-796.

P. 125 **study ... conducted by Australian and Canadian researchers:** Tunstall RJ, Mehan KA, Wadley GD, et al. Exercise training increases lipid metabolism gene expression in human skeletal muscle. *Am J Physiol Endocrinol Metab* 2002;283(1):E66-72.

P. 126 **a Danish and American study about how genes, exercise and diet:** Keller C, Steensberg A, Pilegaard H, et al. Transcriptional activation of the IL-6 gene in human contracting skeletal muscle: influence of muscle glycogen content. *FASEB J* 2001;15(14):2748-2750.

P. 127 **A 2003 study of healthy middle-aged Japanese men and women:** Kimura T, Yokoyama T, Matsumura Y, et al. NOS3 genotype-dependent correlation between blood pressure and physical activity. *Hypertension* 2003;41(2):355-360.

P. 127 **In 2002, Turkish researchers showed:** Gungor K, Beydagi H, Bekir N, et al. The impact of acute dynamic exercise on intraocular pressure: role of the beta 2-adrenergic receptor polymorphism. *J Int Med Res* 2002;30(1):26-33.

P. 127 **according to a 2003 German study, people with certain variants of the vitamin D receptor gene:** Ortlepp JR, Metrikat J, Albrecht M. The vitamin D receptor gene variant and physical activity predicts fasting glucose levels in healthy young men. *Diabet Med* 2003;20(6):451-454.

P. 128 **Italian researchers discovered in 2003:** Pisciotta L, Cantafora A, Piana A, et al. Physical activity modulates effects of some genetic polymorphisms affecting cardiovascular risk in men aged over 40 years. *Nutr Metab Cardiovasc Dis* 2003;13(4):202-210.

P. 132 **Studies show that recreational athletes who engage in endurance sport:** Herrmann M, Schorr H, Obeid R, et al. Homocysteine increases during endurance exercise. *Clin Chem Lab Med* 2003;41(11):1518-1520.

CHAPTER 9

P. 137 **The proverb above from Japan's Okinawa:** Bradley J. Willcox, Craig Willcox, Makoto Suzuki. *The Okinawa Program: How the World's Longest-Lived People Achieve Everlasting Health – And How You Can Too.* Three Rivers Press (paperback), 2002.

P. 139 **Proposed in 1965 by Leonard Hayflick:** Hayflick L. The limited in vitro lifetime of human diploid cell strains. *Exp Cell Res* 1965;37:614-36.

P. 139 **from about 8,000 DNA "letters" at birth to 1,500 in the elderly:** Are telomeres the key to aging and cancer? Genetic Science Learning Center at the University of Utah, http://gslc.genetics.utah.edu/features/telomeres/. Accessed September 28, 2005.

P. 139 **researchers from the University of Utah have found:** *Ibid.*

P. 140 **producing protective proteins in insufficient amounts:** Heydari AR, Wu B, Takahashi R, et al. Expression of heat shock protein 70 is altered by age and diet at the level of transcription. *Mol Cell Biol* 1993;13(5):2909-2918.

P. 140 **generating inappropriate inflammatory substances:** Ershler WB. Interleukin-6: a cytokine for gerontologists. *J Am Geriatr Soc* 1993;41(2):176-181.

P. 140 **Calorie restriction was also shown to prevent many of the changes in gene function:** Finkel T, Holbrook NJ. Oxidants, oxidative stress and the biology of ageing. *Nature* 2000;408:239-247.

P. 140 **mice and rats that consume 25 to 60 percent fewer calories:** Koubova J, Guarente L. How does calorie restriction work? *Genes Dev* 2003;17:313-321.

P. 141 **are much less likely to develop cancer, diabetes and a host of other diseases:** *Ibid.*

P. 141 **short stature, fertility problems and a host of other:** Heilbronn LK, Ravussin E. Calorie restriction and aging: review of the literature and implications for studies in humans. *Am Soc Clin Nutr* 2003;78:361-369.

P. 141 **For example, adults on Okinawa:** *Ibid.*

P. 142 **Radical damage:** This section is based on: Finkel T, Holbrook NJ. Oxidants, oxidative stress and the biology of ageing. *Nature* 2000;408:239-247.

P. 146 **calorie restriction also appears to reduce inflammation:** Chung HY, Kim HJ, Kim JW, Yu BP. The inflammation hypothesis of aging: molecular modulation by calorie restriction. *Ann NY Acad Sci* 2001;928:327-335.

P. 147 **Methyl-group tags that control the way the genes work wander off track:** Richardson B. Impact of aging on DNA methylation. *Aging Res Rev* 2003;2:245–261.

P. 147 **In cancer, for example, misplaced methyl groups:** Santos KF, Mazzola TN, Carvalho HF. The prima donna of epigenetics: the regulation of gene expression by DNA methylation. *Braz J Med Biol Res* 2005;38(10):1531-1541.

P. 147 **believed to contribute to Alzheimer's and Parkinson's:** Mathers JC. Nutrition and epigenetics: how the genome learns from experience. *British Nutrition Foundation Nutrition Bulletin* 2005;30:6-12.

P. 148 **studies suggest that inadequate nutrition in the womb:** *Ibid.*

P. 148 **DNA tends to "remember":** *Ibid.*

P. 148 **in 2004, California researchers showed:** Courtemanche C, Huang AC, Elson-Schwab I, et al. Folate deficiency and ionizing radiation cause DNA breaks in primary human lymphocytes: a comparison. *FASEB J* 2004;18(1):209-211.

P. 149 **antioxidants can even delay age-related disorders of the brain:** Meydani M. Nutrition interventions in age and age-associated disease. *Proc Nutr Soc* 2002;61:165-171.

CHAPTER 10

P. 154 **Americans with Disabilities Act has been extended:** Baker C. Your Genes, Your Choices. Website of the US Department of Energy, www.ornl.gov/sci/techresources/Human_Genome/publicat/genechoice/index.html. Accessed November 17, 2005.

P. 154 **The US Senate has also passed a genetic nondiscrimination bill:** S.306. A Bill to Prohibit Discrimination on the Basis of Genetic Information with Respect to Health Insurance and Employment. Website of the Library of Congress, http://thomas.loc.gov/cgi-bin/bdquery/z?d109:SN00306:@@@L&summ2=m&. Accessed November 23, 2005.

P. 154 **the United Kingdom has a moratorium in place:** Website of BBC News, http://news.bbc.co.uk/1/hi/business/1615397.stm. Accessed November 23, 2005.

Index

S